TWISTED WORD SEARCH

This edition first published in 2018 by Ginger Fox®
an imprint of Hacche Retail Ltd
Stirling House, College Road, Cheltenham GL53 7HY
United Kingdom

www.gingerfox.co.uk

Follow us!
Facebook: GingerFoxUK
Instagram: GingerFoxUK
Twitter: GingerFox_UK

Puzzles created by Dr Gareth Moore at Any Puzzle Media

ISBN: 978-1-911006-39-8

10 9 8 7 6 5 4 3 2 1

Printed and bound in China

What's the TWIST?

Take a standard word search...

E	S	D	A	E	T	F	O	P	U	C	N	O	D	Y	G
G	E	W	T	E	C	E	E	A	M	E	N	O	A	U	N
A	V	T	E	G	T	L	T	A	E	E	C	D	N	R	O
F	I	O	W	R	N	K	N	U	E	T	S	L	O	N	S
O	F	N	T	O	T	A	Q	T	O	E	U	O	E	L	N
G	E	Y	E	I	L	G	X	R	N	C	D	L	E	E	E
N	H	S	I	I	N	I	S	I	K	E	I	G	E	T	E
I	T	D	V	I	S	O	T	Y	H	T	S	K	A	O	T
M	L	E	C	T	R	N	F	T	T	E	D	G	N	M	E
O	L	N	E	D	E	O	T	L	L	N	N	E	E	S	Y
C	A	E	E	L	R	A	E	E	A	E	D	O	N	T	B
D	W	R	A	S	K	D	V	G	D	O	D	I	C	R	D
S	S	V	O	C	U	E	N	R	Z	K	O	U	Y	I	O
N	N	M	O	C	N	U	A	E	F	T	N	A	C	C	O
L	E	N	K	E	O	G	N	Z	W	E	E	L	M	K	G
O	K	K	E	Y	O	F	T	H	E	D	O	O	R	S	S

Find each of the listed words and phrases in the grid. They may be written forwards or backwards in any direction, including diagonally.

Done this before?

Hundreds or **thousands** of times?

Are you ready to try something a little bit DIFFERENT?

...then give it a TWIST!

Find each of the listed words and phrases in the grid. They may be written forwards or backwards in any direction, including diagonally...

..and now comes the INTERESTING bit!

This is an **Empty Inside** word search. Fill in the 36 blank squares in the centre of the grid as you place the words.

E	S	D	A	E	T	F	O	P	U	C	N	O	D	Y	G
G	E	W	T	E	C	E	E	A	M	E	N	O	A	U	N
A	V	T	E	G	T	L	T	A	E	E	C	D	N	R	O
F	I	O	W	R	N	K	N	U	E	T	S	L	O	N	S
O	F	N	T	O	T	A	Q	T	O	E	U	O	E	L	N
G	E	Y	E	I							D	L	E	E	E
N	H	S	I	I							I	G	E	T	E
I	T	D	V	I							S	K	A	O	T
M	L	E	C	T							D	G	N	M	E
O	L	N	E	D							N	E	E	S	Y
C	A	E	E	L							D	O	N	T	B
D	W	R	A	S	K	D	V	G	D	O	D	I	C	R	D
S	S	V	O	C	U	E	N	R	Z	K	O	U	Y	I	O
N	N	M	O	C	N	U	A	E	F	T	N	A	C	C	O
L	E	N	K	E	O	G	N	Z	W	E	E	L	M	K	G
O	K	K	E	Y	O	F	T	H	E	D	O	O	R	S	S

So, are you ready to wreck the **Wraparound**, smash the **Symbolic** and crack the **Little Clues**?

Turn the page to enter the warped world of **TWISTED** word search, featuring a terrifying total of 110 puzzles that bend the rules in 12 deliriously different ways.

Instructions for the puzzles are at the top of each page. If you need more help, **TWIST** the book to read the tips, but only read 'em if you need 'em!

Good luck from the **TWISTED** team... we think you might need it!

Solutions start on page 114!

1. LEFTOVER LETTERS

What's the TWIST?

Find each of the listed **respiratory system** themed words and phrases in the grid. They may be written forwards or backwards in any direction, including diagonally.

Each entry in the grid includes one extra letter (not shown in the word list). Make a note of the extra letter beside the corresponding word or phrase in the list. Then use these letters to spell out a related phrase in the space at the bottom of the page.

TWISTED tip: Grid entries start and end with the correct letter, so search for these letters first.

U	O	X	A	I	R	O	H	T	R	E	L	C	A	N	C
N	C	C	E	B	X	A	X	G	H	P	M	A	U	A	R
B	F	A	L	H	P	F	A	X	H	L	Y	E	R	O	C
R	A	I	Y	O	L	X	M	O	U	T	I	H	V	R	M
A	E	G	E	G	A	C	L	B	I	R	B	O	M	R	R
O	E	D	S	V	E	O	A	V	O	O	O	S	I	Y	B
N	A	I	B	U	Y	R	A	F	N	O	M	L	U	P	N
C	N	A	A	R	L	C	N	D	U	A	G	H	A	O	N
H	L	P	T	E	L	O	I	H	C	N	E	O	R	B	M
U	U	H	S	A	H	O	E	A	L	N	L	X	E	P	L
S	S	R	S	L	X	C	O	B	R	N	L	A	S	A	E
S	N	A	A	I	G	E	A	D	V	T	B	N	E	U	A
E	G	G	D	Y	T	S	H	R	C	L	E	Y	P	X	R
N	I	E	C	R	R	N	A	A	E	E	A	R	I	A	N
L	H	M	A	P	C	A	P	I	L	T	L	A	R	Y	I
O	D	R	R	P	H	A	O	R	Y	N	X	L	E	Y	H

ALVEOLUS
ARTERY
BRONCHIOLE
BRONCHUS
CAPILLARY
CARBON DIOXIDE
DIAPHRAGM

LARYNX
LUNG
MOUTH
NASAL CAVITY
OXYGEN
PHARYNX
PULMONARY

RED BLOOD CELL
RESPIRE
RIBCAGE
THORAX
TRACHEA
VEIN

2. SECRET WORDS

What's the TWIST?

Find each of the listed words and phrases in the grid. They may be written forwards or backwards in any direction, including diagonally.

Each entry in the word list contains at least one concealed **vehicle**; for example CHILDCARE contains a hidden CAR. Delete the hidden vehicles from the words and phrases when searching for them in the grid. So for CHILDCARE search for CHILDE.

ACCIDENT AND EMERGENCY
ADVANTAGE
BLOCKBUSTER
CANTANKEROUS
CHILDCARE
CONSTRAINT
DESCARTES
DWARF PLANET
EXTRACTOR FAN
JETTISON
LIGHTNING STRIKE
SLEIGHT OF HAND
SLOWCOACH
SPROCKETS
STARSTRUCK
SUPRAMOLECULAR
TAXIDERMY
TOUSLED
VOLCANOES
WORSHIPPER

TWISTED tip: Vehicles to look out for include CAR, VAN and ROCKET.

3. WARPED VISION

What's the TWIST?

Find each of the listed **sleep** themed words and phrases in the grid. They may be written forwards or backwards in any direction, including diagonally.

The rows and columns that make up the grid have been twisted, but you should still solve the puzzle as if they were perfectly straight.

Y T W D W S L U G G I S H R S R
R D E U G I T A F T T E I E L L
A K C A S E H T T I H T N T G C
E I E U N W O R N O U T E I I O
W E N R I E O E I T P T G G D A
H E A V Y E Y E D I S N R U T E
T N G N I T S E R Y I A R S G Y
D H D N T W E E S T H D E N R E
R R T R A N C E A T R I I D L T
E L A R I E K N E E S R I F N U
P E Y I T R R L A Y E S C R T H
O R G I N E F M R B G S C R W S
S I R S B E I I M D D T A Y E K
E E U I S N D U K O E I S L O W
D H H T G R L R E I D O Z I N G
E I E I D S W O L L I P R P E B

DOZING
DRAINED
DREAMING
FATIGUED
HEAVY-EYED
HIBERNATING
HIT THE SACK
LETHARGIC
PILLOW
REPOSE
RESTING
SHUT-EYE
SIESTA
SLOW
SLUGGISH
SLUMBERING
TIRED
TRANCE
WEARY
WORN OUT

TWISTED tip: Follow each horizontal, vertical or diagonal line with your finger.

4. SHAPED WORDS

What's the TWIST?

Find each of the listed **teatime** themed words and phrases in the grid.

Each entry in the grid is T-shaped. All entries read from left to right across the top of the T-shape then down the vertical stem of the T. The T-shape itself, however, may be in its usual orientation or rotated by 90, 180 or 270 degrees. One entry is marked as an example.

TWISTED tip: All T-shapes in the grid are sensibly proportioned in terms of width versus height.

BUTTER
CHAMPAGNE
CLOTTED CREAM
CREAM CHEESE
CUCUMBER
~~CUPCAKES~~
DARJEELING
EARL GREY
ENGLISH BREAKFAST
ENGLISH MUFFINS
FINGER SANDWICHES
MACARONS
MILK JUG
NAPKINS
PLATTER
SCONES
SMOKED SALMON
STRAWBERRY JAM
TEACUPS
TEAPOT

What's the TWIST?

Find each of the listed **bingo** themed words and phrases in the grid. They may be written forwards or backwards in any direction, including diagonally.

Fill in the 36 blank squares in the centre of the grid as you place the entries.

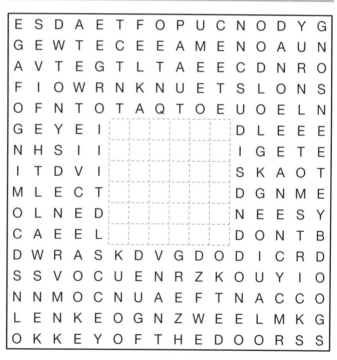

E	S	D	A	E	T	F	O	P	U	C	N	O	D	Y	G
G	E	W	T	E	C	E	E	A	M	E	N	O	A	U	N
A	V	T	E	G	T	L	T	A	E	E	C	D	N	R	O
F	I	O	W	R	N	K	N	U	E	T	S	L	O	N	S
O	F	N	T	O	T	A	Q	T	O	E	U	O	E	L	N
G	E	Y	E	I							D	L	E	E	E
N	H	S	I	I							I	G	E	T	E
I	T	D	V	I							S	K	A	O	T
M	L	E	C	T							D	G	N	M	E
O	L	N	E	D							N	E	E	S	Y
C	A	E	E	L							D	O	N	T	B
D	W	R	A	S	K	D	V	G	D	O	D	I	C	R	D
S	S	V	O	C	U	E	N	R	Z	K	O	U	Y	I	O
N	N	M	O	C	N	U	A	E	F	T	N	A	C	C	O
L	E	N	K	E	O	G	N	Z	W	E	E	L	M	K	G
O	K	K	E	Y	O	F	T	H	E	D	O	O	R	S	S

ALL THE FIVES
COMING OF AGE
CUP OF TEA
DANCING QUEEN
DOCTOR'S ORDERS
GARDEN GATE
GOODBYE TEENS
KEY OF THE DOOR
KNOCK AT THE DOOR
LEGS ELEVEN
MAN ALIVE
ONE DOZEN
ONE LITTLE DUCK
SWEET SIXTEEN
TOM'S TRICKS
TONY'S DEN
TWO LITTLE DUCKS
UNLUCKY FOR SOME
VALENTINE'S DAY
YOUNG AND KEEN

TWISTED tip: Start with the longest entries – you won't be able to tell where some of the shorter ones fit until you have placed others.

6. WRAPAROUND

What's the TWIST?

Find each of the listed **breeds of cat** in the grid. They may be written forwards or backwards in any direction, including diagonally.

Entries can wrap around from one edge of the grid to the other, so imagine that the grid repeats immediately on all sides. Breed names that wrap around continue on the opposite side to correspond with where they would be on the repeated grid. One entry is marked as an example.

E	M	O	P	Y	L	I	A	T	B	O	B	G	N	O	K
R	L	H	B	N	M	I	G	E	L	O	L	J	R	S	N
N	Y	L	L	I	T	N	A	H	C	J	B	T	E	L	N
N	R	R	D	R	X	I	X	A	L	U	H	B	X	S	O
N	A	L	T	S	I	E	S	R	R	A	O	R	A	S	X
T	R	A	H	C	I	U	E	M	I	E	N	X	U	E	R
R	O	B	N	I	E	T	E	R	N	I	A	D	E	A	P
E	M	Y	Y	G	L	S	O	B	E	B	I	K	E	R	M
N	R	S	G	G	E	E	E	R	A	B	R	A	N	R	H
S	A	S	N	E	X	X	M	M	T	I	E	O	E	E	O
G	I	I	I	O	R	R	B	A	A	O	B	O	O	E	P
L	I	N	T	A	N	I	E	N	I	I	I	I	O	T	G
B	T	I	R	P	N	M	J	X	H	N	S	S	R	X	Y
A	C	A	K	O	Y	J	A	V	A	N	E	S	E	A	T
S	E	N	Y	N	C	G	N	M	S	H	N	C	G	S	L
G	L	E	A	S	H	O	E	I	S	E	A	S	O	M	H

TWISTED tip: Try to work out why the word SPHYNX is shown as it is.

ABYSSINIAN
BAMBINO
BURMESE
CHANTILLY
CHARTREUX
CORNISH REX
EGYPTIAN MAU
EXOTIC SHORTHAIR
HIGHLANDER
JAVANESE
MAINE COON
MANX
MEKONG BOBTAIL
OREGON REX
PERSIAN
SIAMESE
SIBERIAN
~~SPHYNX~~
TORTOISESHELL
TOYGER

7. SYMBOLIC

What's the TWIST?

Find each of the listed words and phrases in the grid. They may be written forwards or backwards in any direction, including diagonally.

Each word and phrase listed contains a **number**; for example ARTWORK contains a hidden TWO. Replace the numbers with their corresponding digits when searching for them in the grid. So for ARTWORK search for AR2RK.

TWISTED tip: Multi-digit numbers (for example, TEN) appear as multiple digits in the grid too (10).

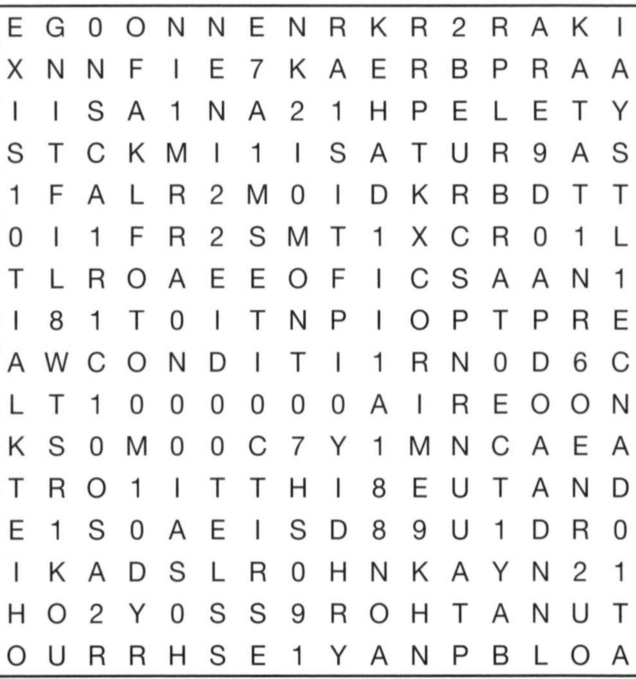

E	G	0	O	N	N	E	N	R	K	R	2	R	A	K	I
X	N	N	F	I	E	7	K	A	E	R	B	P	R	A	A
I	I	S	A	1	N	A	2	1	H	P	E	L	E	T	Y
S	T	C	K	M	I	1	I	S	A	T	U	R	9	A	S
1	F	A	L	R	2	M	0	I	D	K	R	B	D	T	T
0	I	1	F	R	2	S	M	T	1	X	C	R	0	1	L
T	L	R	O	A	E	E	O	F	I	C	S	A	A	N	1
I	8	1	T	0	I	T	N	P	I	O	P	T	P	R	E
A	W	C	O	N	D	I	T	I	1	R	N	0	D	6	C
L	T	1	0	0	0	0	0	0	A	I	R	E	O	O	N
K	S	0	M	0	0	C	7	Y	1	M	N	C	A	E	A
T	R	O	1	I	T	T	H	I	8	E	U	T	A	N	D
E	1	S	0	A	E	I	S	D	8	9	U	1	D	R	0
I	K	A	D	S	L	R	0	H	N	K	A	Y	N	2	1
H	O	2	Y	0	S	S	9	R	O	H	T	A	N	U	T
O	U	R	R	H	S	E	1	Y	A	N	P	B	L	O	A

AIRFREIGHT
ARTWORK
ATTENDANCE
BAYONET
BREAKS EVEN
CONDITIONER
EXISTENTIAL
HEIGHTENED
INTENTION
LATENT
MILLIONAIRE
MONEY
NETWORK
OUTWORN
POSTWOMAN
SATURNINE
SIX-PACK
TELEPHONE
THORNINESS
WEIGHTLIFTING

8. CROSS WORDS

What's the TWIST?

Find each of the listed words and phrases in the grid.

Each entry in the grid is cross-shaped – either X or +. The letter at the centre of each cross-shape (U in this case) is used twice. All entries in the grid read horizontally from left to right for the first half of the word or phrase, then from top to bottom for the second half. One entry is marked as an example.

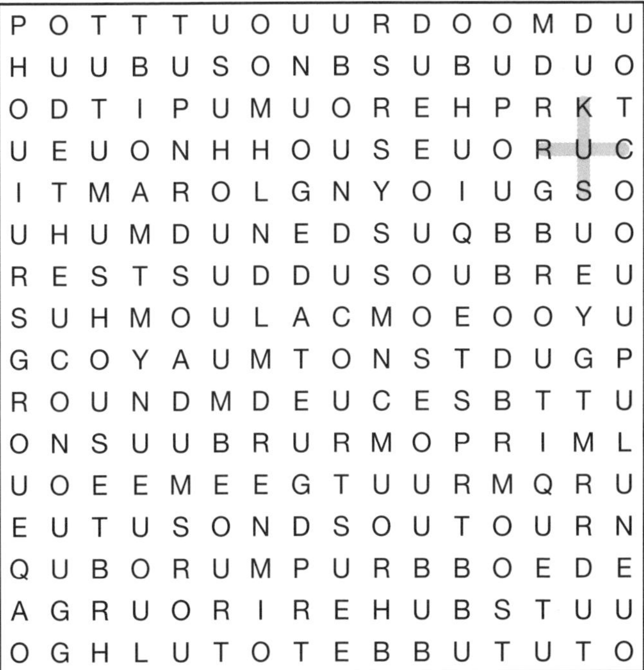

P	O	T	T	T	U	O	U	U	R	D	O	O	M	D	U
H	U	U	B	U	S	O	N	B	S	U	B	U	D	U	O
O	D	T	I	P	U	M	U	O	R	E	H	P	R	K	T
U	E	U	O	N	H	H	O	U	S	E	U	O	R	U	C
I	T	M	A	R	O	L	G	N	Y	O	I	U	G	S	O
U	H	U	M	D	U	N	E	D	S	U	Q	B	B	U	O
R	E	S	T	S	U	D	D	U	S	O	U	B	R	E	U
S	U	H	M	O	U	L	A	C	M	O	E	O	O	Y	U
G	C	O	Y	A	U	M	T	O	N	S	T	D	U	G	P
R	O	U	N	D	M	D	E	U	C	E	S	B	T	T	U
O	N	S	U	U	B	R	U	R	M	O	P	R	I	M	L
U	O	E	E	M	E	E	G	T	U	U	R	M	Q	R	U
E	U	T	U	S	O	N	D	S	O	U	T	O	U	R	N
Q	U	B	O	R	U	M	P	U	R	B	B	O	E	D	E
A	G	R	U	O	R	I	R	E	H	U	B	S	T	U	U
O	G	H	L	U	T	O	T	E	B	B	U	T	U	T	O

TWISTED tip: Sometimes two entries share a central letter. One entry will be X-shaped and one will be +-shaped.

AUTEUR
BUST-UP
BUYOUT
DEUCE COURT
DUGOUT
HOUSEBOUND
HUBBUB
HUMMUS
HUMOUR
LOUNGE SUIT
MAUSOLEUMS
OUTPUT
PURSUE
ROUNDHOUSE
~~RUCKUS~~
RUMOUR
SOUBRIQUET
SUBDUE
TOURNIQUET
YOUNG ADULT

9. LEFTOVER LETTERS

What's the TWIST?

Find each of the listed **courtroom** themed words in the grid. They may be written forwards or backwards in any direction, including diagonally.

Each entry in the grid includes one extra letter (not shown in the word list). Make a note of the extra letter beside the corresponding word in the list. Then use the letters to spell out a related phrase in the space at the bottom of the page.

TWISTED tip: Longer grid entries are less changed by the addition of an extra letter, so are easier to spot.

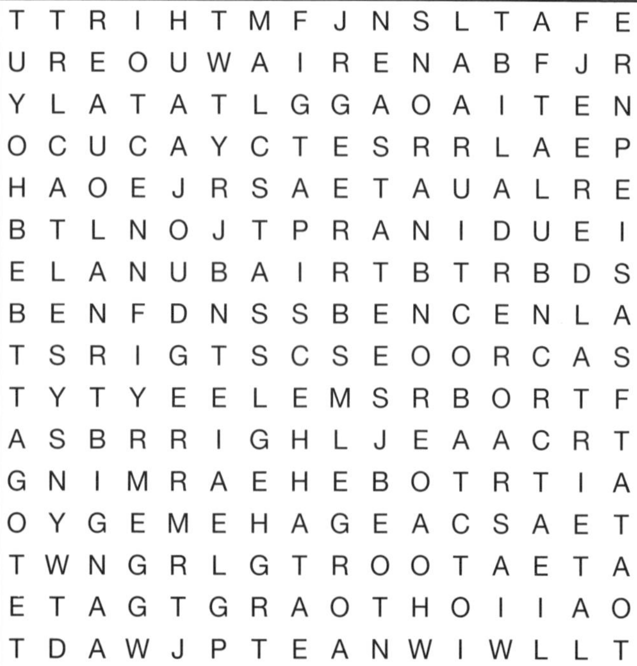

AGENT
AGREEMENT
ARBITRATE
ASSETS
BARRISTER
CLIENT
CONTRACT
COUNSEL
DAMAGES
ESTATE
FRAUD
HEARING
JUDGE
JURY
LIABLE
NOTARY
PROBATE
SCAM
TRIBUNAL
WILL

....

10. LITTLE CLUES

What's the TWIST?

The names of 20 **colours** are hidden in the grid. They may be written forwards or backwards in any direction, including diagonally.

Work out what the colours are with the help of the initial letters given. The initials are listed alphabetically, which should help when there is more than one entry starting with the same letter.

I U O U N E W O L L E Y T V E L
W T A V E E B A L Q Y V A A R G
O D Q U E E O R S E V I L O A N
C C U G R G V I O E Y E I M E I
I I A O G D L R W W L A L E A B
N W M L R V A G L H N A S Q N M
D M A D E N N A Q V I I C L I A
I P R R G E K O G E O T A G I G
G I I E I C T N H U M A E R C E
O N N I A T R Q Q Q N L L G D N
E K E L E M G R T C N I E L O T
O A B L S L U O U A G V G G E A
A O O R L T I V I E N A E R K E
E I S E N N B L U E U Q I A E E
V N E D H I R T A A U Q C E M E
O H A E C U N G O C R O A T T L

TWISTED tip: The first colour in the word list is AQUAMARINE; the other words are all between three and nine letters long.

A..
B..
B..
B..
C..
G..
G..
I..
L..
M..
O..
O..
P..
R..
S..
T..
T..
V..
W..
Y..

11. SECRET WORDS

What's the TWIST?

Find each of the listed words and phrases in the grid. They may be written forwards or backwards in any direction, including diagonally.

Each entry in the word list contains at least one concealed **flying bird**; for example CONTRAVENE contains a hidden RAVEN. Delete the hidden birds from the words and phrases when searching for them in the grid. So for CONTRAVENE search for CONTE.

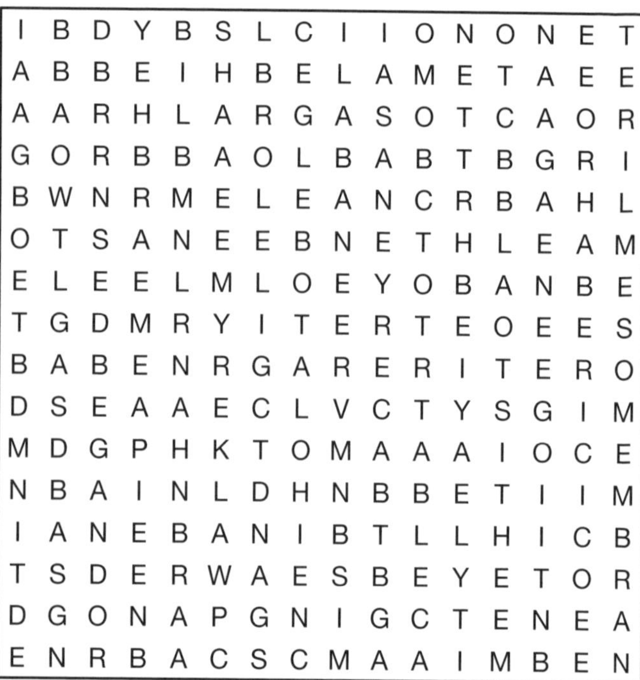

ACKNOWLEDGE
BIODIVERSITY
BOTSWANA
BROOKLYN
CHUFFING
CONTRAVENE
DISROBING
GOOSEBERRY
GULLIBLE
HANDOVER
INTERNATIONAL
JAYWALKER
PARTITION
REGRETTABLE
SCOOTER
SHAGREEN
SPREADEAGLED
THE ACHERON
TOMAHAWK
TRUFFLE

TWISTED tip: If you can't find a bird within a particular word, search for the word in the grid then work out what's missing.

12. EMPTY INSIDE

What's the TWIST?

Find each of the listed **break time** themed words and phrases in the grid. They may be written forwards or backwards in any direction, including diagonally.

Fill in the 36 blank squares in the centre of the grid as you place the entries.

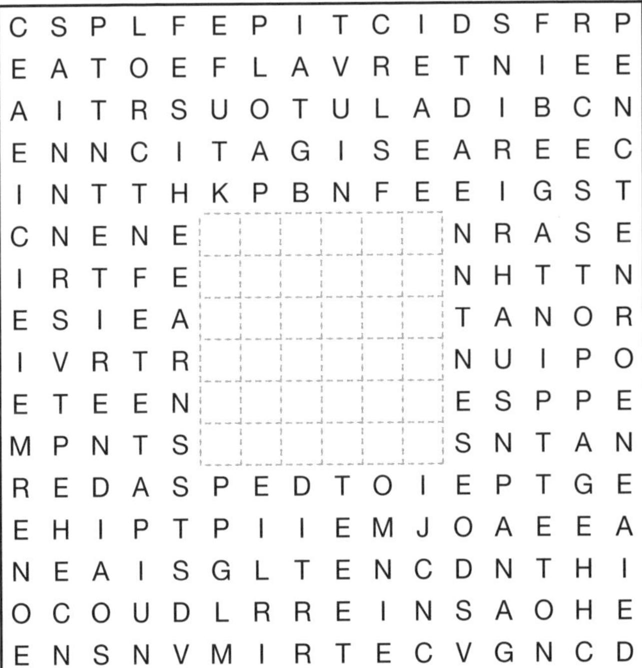

ADJOURNMENT
BREATHING SPACE
CATCH YOUR BREATH
DEFERMENT
DELIBERATE
INTERLUDE
INTERMISSION
INTERRUPTION
INTERVAL
PAUSE
POSTPONEMENT
PUTTING-OFF
RECESS
REMISSION
RESPITE
STANDSTILL
STOPPAGE
STRIKE
SUSPENSION
TAKE FIVE

TWISTED tip: If you find that you can't fit all of the entries in the grid, you have probably made a mistake in the puzzle's empty heart.

What's the TWIST?

Find each of the listed **types of flying bird** in the grid.

Each entry in the grid is shaped like a flying bird. Bird-shapes may read from left to right or from right to left, but are never rotated. They are always symmetrical in shape with a dipped centre. One entry is marked as an example.

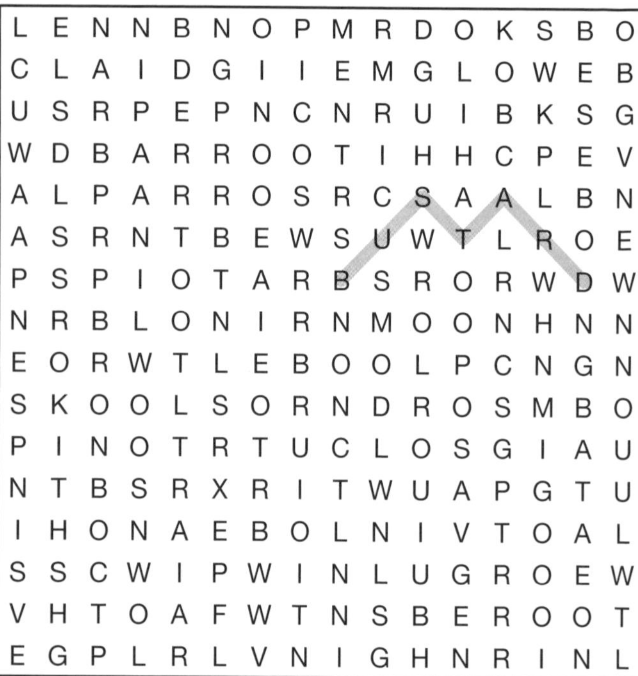

L E N N B N O P M R D O K S B O
C L A I D G I I E M G L O W E B
U S R P E P N C N R U I B K S G
W D B A R R O O T I H H C P E V
A L P A R R O S R C S A A L B N
A S R N T B E W S U W T L R O E
P S P I O T A R B S R O R W D W
N R B L O N I R N M O O N H N N
E O R W T L E B O O L P C N G N
S K O O L S O R N D R O S M B O
P I N O T R T U C L O S G I A U
N T B S R X R I T W U A P G T U
I H O N A E B O L N I V T O A L
S S C W I P W I N L U G R O E W
V H T O A F W T N S B E R O O T
E G P L R L V N I G H N R I N L

TWISTED tip: As the bird-shapes are symmetrical, the first letter will always be on the same row as the last letter.

ALBATROSS
BITTERN
~~BUSTARD~~
CHICKEN
CORMORANT
GOLDCREST
GOOSE

HERON
HUMMINGBIRD
LAPWING
ROBIN
SANDPIPER
SNOWFINCH
SPARROW

SPOONBILL
STORK
SWALLOW
VULTURE
WAGTAIL
WAXBILL

14. THIS AND THAT

What's the TWIST?

Find each of the listed missing words in the grid. They may be written forwards or backwards in any direction, including diagonally.

First complete each entry in the word list to make a well-known phrase. For example, AS AND .... completes as AS AND WHEN, so you must then search for WHEN in the grid.

L	T	H	O	U	D	U	R	I	I	T	G	A	R	A	S
O	T	E	E	I	C	G	W	L	S	D	T	E	R	P	T
H	R	G	O	O	G	H	H	T	U	P	B	H	A	P	L
E	A	V	K	E	I	I	R	E	A	O	E	N	R	I	N
H	S	E	F	T	R	I	W	I	I	D	S	E	C	I	Y
H	S	S	E	O	P	T	S	A	C	S	D	N	A	E	F
E	E	K	S	E	R	R	S	O	H	R	E	R	F	S	S
E	T	T	S	W	E	T	G	A	R	P	E	I	E	W	O
E	H	H	H	T	S	R	H	W	F	S	W	A	N	S	R
D	D	E	A	T	A	E	D	M	F	K	K	H	M	I	S
N	N	W	K	T	E	O	O	A	E	O	A	K	M	R	S
D	R	F	R	I	T	O	D	I	M	M	U	E	E	F	N
H	H	O	O	T	R	E	A	R	S	O	D	N	R	Y	S
S	M	K	A	G	A	S	O	F	L	G	R	H	D	B	C
S	E	G	P	T	Y	M	S	E	N	O	G	H	I	O	N
T	B	H	H	P	E	U	E	S	H	S	H	E	E	D	N

AS AND ....
BACK AND ....
BACON AND ....
BED AND ....
BLACK AND ....
BODY AND ....
BREAD AND ....
BRICKS AND ....
BRIDE AND ....
LIFE AND ....
LOCK AND ....
LOST AND ....
MAN AND ....
NAME AND ....
NULL AND ....
PEACHES AND..............................
PEN AND ....
POTS AND ....
STARS AND ....
WAIT AND ....

TWISTED tip: If you're not sure how to complete a phrase, look in the grid for likely answers.

15. LEFTOVER LETTERS

What's the TWIST?

Find each of the listed **happiness** themed words in the grid. They may be written forwards or backwards in any direction, including diagonally.

Each entry in the grid includes one extra letter (not shown in the word list). Make a note of the extra letter beside the corresponding word in the list. Then use the letters to spell out a related phrase in the space at the bottom of the page.

TWISTED tip: Guessing the hidden phrase early on will help you work out which letter has been added to each word.

O	I	L	E	L	A	N	T	E	D	T	O	S	L	T	R
E	E	M	U	N	I	Y	S	E	N	A	T	U	L	T	I
G	D	U	C	A	L	D	I	A	V	N	L	O	U	I	M
I	S	F	C	L	E	F	I	E	A	D	D	R	C	D	C
R	I	Y	O	U	S	D	R	N	C	R	O	U	I	E	I
A	I	O	D	I	A	J	R	D	H	T	Y	T	T	R	R
A	J	J	E	T	O	E	U	E	E	L	S	P	N	L	I
Y	O	T	R	Y	B	E	Y	I	E	C	M	O	A	L	O
D	A	R	E	U	D	E	L	F	R	O	A	A	T	I	H
S	F	D	X	H	R	U	G	I	G	R	I	R	S	R	P
I	A	E	I	R	F	P	L	T	F	N	L	S	C	H	U
L	R	L	E	F	P	A	A	R	U	T	I	I	E	T	E
E	O	M	E	I	E	A	G	A	L	E	N	N	O	L	T
P	L	E	R	A	S	E	D	R	D	N	G	T	O	S	R
Y	L	S	E	M	O	E	M	G	I	T	E	O	P	L	A
G	A	C	L	D	E	T	H	I	G	I	L	E	D	D	Y

CHEERFUL
CONTENT
DELIGHTED
ECSTATIC
ELATED
EUPHORIC
EXUBERANT
GLAD
GLEEFUL
GRATIFIED
JOLLY
JOYFUL
MERRY
OVERJOYED
PLEASED
RADIANT
RAPTUROUS
SATISFIED
SMILING
THRILLED

16. LITTLE CLUES

What's the TWIST?

The names of 20 **capital cities** are hidden in the grid. They may be written forwards or backwards in any direction, including diagonally.

Work out what the cities are with the help of the initial letters given. The initials are listed alphabetically, which should help when there is more than one entry starting with the same letter.

```
A R R E B N A C C C H T H N E O
M L O N D O N I G N I J I E B B
A M S T E R D A M M A E A T E N
I A T O A L W L W K O S M R B N
L S R N C E A S E C E A L R A S
E D I D H O S O R I D I U T A T
O N N R D E H H D R N S H T N O
C E C W A O I I I B S E D I L C
I G O M T P N D E E N U P K U K
R A R O A I G M L S B C M N O H
J H I Y L G T S C L O R R I E O
B N A K O M O C I E O R L S S L
L E C O L M N N N M A O O L S M
E P N T T J D C E O N D G E S H
S O E R M T C M O S C O W H M M
O C H R B U D A P E S T T A S T
```

A...
A...
B...
B...
B...
B...
C...
C...
C...
D...
H...
L...
M...
M...
P...
R...
S...
S...
T...
W...................D...................

TWISTED tip: The cities are all capitals of major countries including China, Egypt and Australia.

17. SHAPED WORDS

What's the TWIST?

Find each of the listed **square meal** themed words and phrases in the grid.

Each entry in the grid is square-shaped, always reading clockwise and starting from one of the four corners. One entry is marked as an example.

TWISTED tip: All square-shapes in the grid have three sides of the same length, but one less letter on the fourth side.

BEEF
CALZONE PIZZA
CHEESEBURGER
CHICKEN KORMA
~~CHOW MEIN~~
EGG-FRIED RICE
JACKET POTATO
LAMB RUMP
MOUSSAKA
PANCAKES
PORK SHOULDER
PORRIDGE
SANDWICH
SAUSAGES
SHEPHERD'S PIE
SOUVLAKI
STEW
TOFU
WRAP
YAKI SOBA

18. VOWELLESS

What's the TWIST?

Find each of the listed words in the grid. They may be written forwards or backwards in any direction, including diagonally.

Ignore all vowels (in this case they are mainly the letter I) in the words when searching in the grid. So for BIKINI search for BKN.

L	B	H	V	N	Z	G	R	Y	H	B	T	L	R	S	V
V	G	G	T	V	N	Y	G	S	G	M	D	T	N	H	N
S	R	G	C	Y	D	D	T	N	M	F	P	B	D	Y	B
L	Y	G	F	N	F	R	T	N	S	H	Y	L	L	B	L
N	B	C	D	N	B	B	S	G	D	L	H	B	C	D	D
G	L	G	S	F	H	G	G	B	P	G	S	L	H	T	L
S	Y	H	T	N	Y	M	Y	H	L	V	T	N	R	M	R
H	N	T	L	D	L	N	G	T	D	T	T	S	L	V	Y
G	L	G	S	L	S	N	G	N	L	G	Y	N	N	T	M
T	B	N	G	V	M	N	F	N	H	V	N	B	B	G	M
Y	T	K	B	N	T	T	H	P	L	S	C	S	H	H	G
N	T	D	B	M	T	M	B	B	L	S	N	N	L	T	N
L	P	L	B	Y	S	R	R	L	T	G	G	M	G	V	B
P	S	B	B	R	D	G	P	P	T	S	R	N	D	Y	C
S	N	R	D	S	L	T	K	S	D	Y	K	M	R	C	G
G	Z	T	Z	N	V	S	G	H	D	B	T	M	G	Y	N

TWISTED tip: Look for any double letters in the grid, especially those formed by the removal of vowels from the listed words.

BIKINI
BRITISH
CIVILISING
DIGITISING
DIMINISHING
DISINHIBITS
DISPIRITING
FINISHING
ILLIMITABILITY
IMBIBING
IMPLICIT
INCIVILITY
INDIVISIBLY
INHIBITING
PILGRIM
PRIMITIVIST
RIGIDIFYING
RISIBILITY
SILICIFYING
VISIBILITY

19. WARPED VISION

What's the TWIST?

Find each of the listed **emotions** themed words in the grid. They may be written forwards or backwards in any direction, including diagonally.

The rows and columns that make up the grid have been twisted, but you should still solve the puzzle as if they were perfectly straight.

TWISTED tip: Try starting in the centre of the grid where it is less distorted.

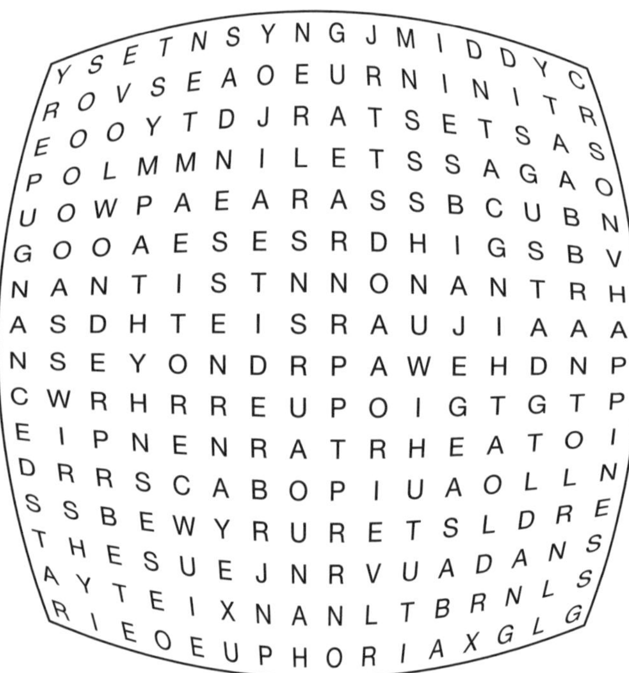

ABHORRENCE
ALARM
ANXIETY
AWE
DISGUST
DISTASTE
EUPHORIA
GRATITUDE
HAPPINESS
HORROR
INTEREST
JOY
LOATHING
LOVE
PANIC
REPUGNANCE
SADNESS
SURPRISE
SYMPATHY
WONDER

20. VOWELLESS

What's the TWIST?

Find each of the listed words and phrases in the grid. They may be written forwards or backwards in any direction, including diagonally.

Ignore all vowels (in this case they are all the letter A) in the words and phrases when searching in the grid. So for BALACLAVA search for BLCLV.

P D N B C N R P G N L N B D R P
B P B D P S T G M S R G G M S M
P B B Y G R N D T N N R M S B S
P M T K B C D Y R H B M B K C C
R K N D N C V L S R M M Y B B Y
M C L J P B P L P G M N F P K H
C L B B C C L N L R S H P R R C
H B C S K R V D R S W B B R N N
B Y T S N R C R F R D Y S L W B
G R F N Y M M M P D K B B G S C
V K C N P P K D J S M S R K D K
N D S D M J P M N M C M M L S L
W B M S B Y Y H B B M M C M B S
C W C P H R M N S R S L N D R H
K R L B M C W D D L K K M D G R
N B B D C B D R N B B L C L V C

TWISTED tip: Look for the rarest letters in the grid first, such as the J.

AARDVARKS
ABRACADABRA
ALABAMA
ANAGRAM
ANKARA
AS HAPPY AS A CLAM
BABY GRAND
BABY MAMA
BACKLASH
BALACLAVA
BANAL
CANADA
CASABLANCA
DAMASK
FARADAY'S LAW
GRAMMAR
JAPAN
PAGAN
PANAMA HAT
RAMADAN

21. LEFTOVER LETTERS

What's the TWIST?

Find each of the listed **famous singers** in the grid. They may be written forwards or backwards in any direction, including diagonally.

Each entry in the grid includes one extra letter (not shown in the word list). Make a note of the extra letter beside the corresponding name in the list. Then use the letters to spell out a related phrase in the space at the bottom of the page.

S	R	D	A	N	E	H	Y	Y	E	O	A	E	S	F	Y
H	M	Y	J	Y	S	R	M	T	N	N	P	N	R	E	T
A	S	O	J	D	E	T	T	A	N	O	H	E	B	A	P
K	R	B	I	O	N	T	L	N	S	O	U	A	K	R	C
E	A	Y	M	C	T	A	P	Y	J	D	F	B	I	O	R
I	E	I	K	S	H	H	V	M	D	I	O	F	T	I	A
R	P	A	A	R	T	A	N	I	S	K	N	N	A	R	F
A	S	L	E	O	F	O	E	L	D	C	O	H	N	N	B
B	Y	C	E	I	T	M	E	L	E	B	A	E	K	A	O
R	E	E	F	L	E	D	A	C	J	N	O	F	K	E	F
O	N	I	E	R	E	D	L	I	N	A	N	W	Y	E	B
N	T	B	C	C	M	A	W	A	W	I	C	O	I	O	D
I	I	U	H	E	M	S	O	S	P	E	O	K	N	E	Y
Y	R	E	R	E	P	Y	T	A	K	E	P	Y	S	D	L
Y	E	L	S	E	R	P	S	I	V	I	L	E	E	O	A
R	B	E	T	E	O	R	R	M	D	L	B	S	B	B	N

ADELE
BEYONCÉ
BOB DYLAN
BONO
BRITNEY SPEARS
CHER
DAVID BOWIE
ELTON JOHN
ELVIS PRESLEY
FRANK SINATRA
FREDDIE MERCURY
JOHN LENNON
KATY PERRY
MADONNA
MICHAEL JACKSON
PINK
PRINCE
RIHANNA
SEAL
SHAKIRA

TWISTED tip: Shorter words have fewer places in which additional letters can be added. Try searching for them with various gap permutations.

22. VOWELLESS

What's the TWIST?

Find each of the listed words and phrases in the grid. They may be written forwards or backwards in any direction, including diagonally.

Ignore all vowels (in this case they are all the letter E) in the words and phrases when searching in the grid. So for EMBEZZLEMENT search for MBZZLMNT.

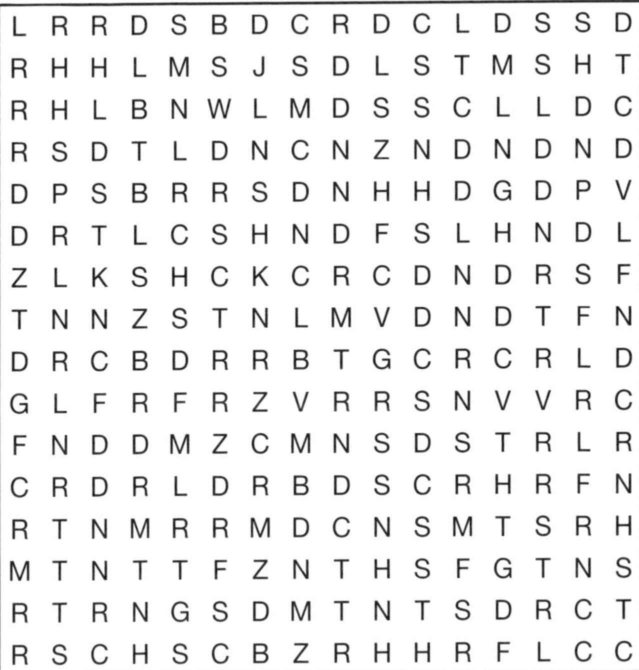

L	R	R	D	S	B	D	C	R	D	C	L	D	S	S	D
R	H	H	L	M	S	J	S	D	L	S	T	M	S	H	T
R	H	L	B	N	W	L	M	D	S	S	C	L	L	D	C
R	S	D	T	L	D	N	C	N	Z	N	D	N	D	N	D
D	P	S	B	R	R	S	D	N	H	H	D	G	D	P	V
D	R	T	L	C	S	H	N	D	F	S	L	H	N	D	L
Z	L	K	S	H	C	K	C	R	C	D	N	D	R	S	F
T	N	N	Z	S	T	N	L	M	V	D	N	D	T	F	N
D	R	C	B	D	R	R	B	T	G	C	R	C	R	L	D
G	L	F	R	F	R	Z	V	R	R	S	N	V	V	R	C
F	N	D	D	M	Z	C	M	N	S	D	S	T	R	L	R
C	R	D	R	L	D	R	B	D	S	C	R	H	R	F	N
R	T	N	M	R	R	M	D	C	N	S	M	T	S	R	H
M	T	N	T	T	F	Z	N	T	H	S	F	G	T	N	S
R	T	R	N	G	S	D	M	T	N	T	S	D	R	C	T
R	S	C	H	S	C	B	Z	R	H	H	R	F	L	C	C

BEECH TREE
BESEECHED
CRÈME DE MENTHE
DEFENCELESS
DEFERENCE
DEFERRED
DEPENDENCE
DESCENDED
EFFERVESCENT
EMBEZZLEMENT
ESTEEMED
GREEN SCREEN
HEEDLESS
HELTER-SKELTER
JEWEL BEETLE
NERVE CENTRE
NEVERTHELESS
REDRESSED
RE-EMERGED
TEETERED

TWISTED tip: Only one letter in this grid is used by more than one entry.

23. CROSS WORDS

What's the TWIST?

Find each of the listed words and phrases in the grid.

Each entry in the grid is cross-shaped – either **X** or **+**. The letter at the centre of each cross-shape (R in this case) is used twice. All entries in the grid read horizontally from left to right for the first half of the word or phrase, then from top to bottom for the second half.

TWISTED tip: For each cross, the first half will always read either left to right or diagonally from bottom-left to top-right.

H R S E B R U P H U V E P A T I
E R A E E T D A E I E H D R R P
R A S T R A W F P E R S E B I S
Y U F A R Y A B E R E R S R A R
R A I I Y A T E R A S D E R A E
T E R R A R U I I A R P T D A L
Y F M S E N R A P O U C S D R E
R T A S R C E R W U R R H A Y Y
T M U T U I D A S H C A E O E R
R C S R T S E S C E C R P R I A
T R T E A U E I A R U O A Y A I
T S R A P L R M N B U H G T D I
U U D I O T R E A T T A B R S R
S R R U S R I U S R E T A E A D
O C E A E U S E I R K C K R R M
S B E R L R S B R H T S U O F S

ARTERY
BIRTHMARKS
BRIARS
BUREAUCRAT
CARDIOGRAM
DREARY
ENRAPTURED
ERRORS
FRIARS
ORDERS
ORDURE
PERIPHERAL
PERSEVERES
PRIORY
SCRIPTURAL
STRAWBERRY
STRICTURES
STRUCTURAL
TERRA FIRMA
WORD SEARCH

24. SECRET WORDS

What's the TWIST?

Find each of the listed words and phrases in the grid. They may be written forwards or backwards in any direction, including diagonally.

Each entry in the word list contains at least one concealed **body of water**; for example BOMBAY DUCK contains a hidden BAY. Delete the hidden bodies of water from the words and phrases when searching for them in the grid. So for BOMBAY DUCK search for BOMDUCK.

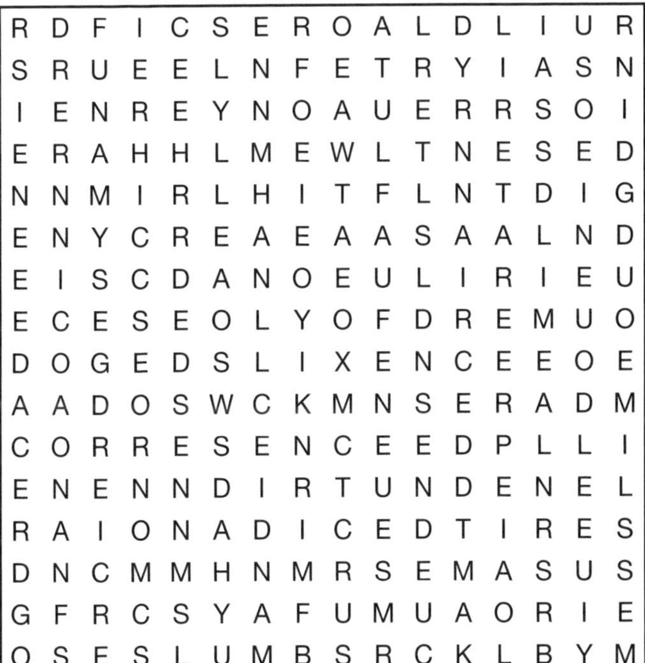

R D F I C S E R O A L D L I U R
S R U E E L N F E T R Y I A S N
I E N R E Y N O A U E R R S O I
E R A H H L M E W L T N E S E D
N N M I R L H I T F L N T D I G
E N Y C R E A E A A S A A L N D
E I S C D A N O E U L I R I E U
E C E S E O L Y O F D R E M U O
D O G E D S L I X E N C E E O E
A A D O S W C K M N S E R A D M
C O R R E S E N C E E D P L L I
E N E N N D I R T U N D E N E L
R A I O N A D I C E D T I R E S
D N C M M H N M R S E M A S U S
G F R C S Y A F U M U A O R I E
O S E S L U M B S R C K L B Y M

TWISTED tip: Start with the longest word or phrase listed, and work out how many letters you need to delete to fit it in the grid.

ALIMENTARY CANAL
BOMBAY DUCK
BROOKLYNITE
BUS DRIVER
CORRESPONDENCE
DESPONDENT
DISCOVERY
DISEASE
ENGULFING
FALSE ALARM
FLAT SEASON
HEAT-SEAL
MAINSTREAM MEDIA
PREPONDERATE
ROD BAYONET
SCREWDRIVER
SLAKED LIME
SNOWFLAKES
STREAM OF CONSCIOUSNESS
UNDERCOVER

25. WRAPAROUND

What's the TWIST?

Find each of the listed **Grand Prix tracks** in the grid. They may be written forwards or backwards in any direction, including diagonally.

Entries can wrap around from one edge of the grid to the other, so imagine that the grid repeats immediately on all sides. Track names that wrap around continue on the opposite side to correspond with where they would be on the repeated grid.

```
E A S O I H E V U N K N A E C D
J G H H S K N U A K I T E B C R
N I N O D L U H K R A P N O T G
S O N H I I S Y M L S N I N S A
R B G R A L M I U I C M I M P T
E A R A N C E N J U A A O E A G
G R N A I H Y U N A R N S N N L
A A R A N A F A I H A E B I Z D
O Y L E D D A R A C M U R P L A
H B K D I R S B O R L G G I R V
E C N P A C R H T P R S B C E G
O R A G N U H I A U N H G N I R
A Y S S A M C R B T H K N I T H
A A O T P S K R I R C O A P E G
I G O B O E U D I N N H A N A W
B E L E L N K Z G A G R G C D A
```

TWISTED tip: Try copying the far-left column of letters into the space to the right of the grid, and vice versa. Then copy the top row of letters into the space below the grid, and vice versa.

AINTREE
ALBERT PARK
BAHRAIN
BRANDS HATCH
CATALUNYA
DONINGTON PARK
FUJI SPEEDWAY
HOCKENHEIMRING
HUNGARORING
INDIANAPOLIS
ISTANBUL PARK
KYALAMI
MONACO
MONZA
NURBURGRING
OSTERREICHRING
SEPANG
SHANGHAI
SILVERSTONE
SUZUKA

26. LITTLE CLUES

What's the TWIST?

The names of 20 **countries** are hidden in the grid. They may be written forwards or backwards in any direction, including diagonally.

Work out the names of the countries with the help of the initial letters given. The initials are listed alphabetically, which should help when there is more than one entry starting with the same letter.

B R R T H L N F A I R E G I N E
I L A G U T R O P A N L E D X I
I I A K A U E G I H U A N D I L
K R A M N E D D A A I A N N I U
E B A U I A O N N P L A I G A N
L A N O M B I I O R L R A U N A
D I L E M H B I E I A T X G D T
E R B A C A H Z A Q T F A E D O
R E C B C T T H A I B M A G I I
O G W H E I T F I N L A N D A E
P L A G W G R U O B M E X U L L
A A R S C A A H C N M E X I C O
G Z I M B A B W E T I A N K Z A
N M F R A N C E T B T A N M E I
I N A T S I N A H G F A P A O E
S G E N I A R K U M I R O S I T

TWISTED tip: There is one four-letter country in this grid. The longest country name has eleven letters.

A...
A...
C...
C...
D...
E...
F...
F...
G...
I...
L...
M...
N...
P...
S...
S...
S...
T...
U...
Z...

27. LEFTOVER LETTERS

What's the TWIST?

Find each of the listed **types of vehicle** in the grid. They may be written forwards or backwards in any direction, including diagonally.

Each entry in the grid includes one extra letter (not shown in the word list). Make a note of the extra letter beside the corresponding vehicle name in the list. Then use the letters to spell out a related phrase in the space at the bottom of the page.

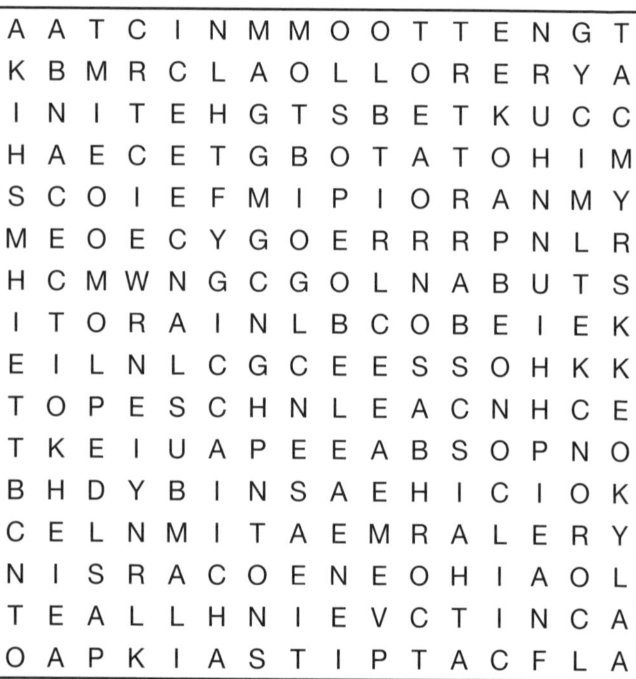

AMBULANCE
BICYCLE
BOAT
BUS
CAR
CHARIOT
COACH
FIRE ENGINE
HELICOPTER
LORRY
MOPED
MOTORBIKE
PLANE
ROCKET
SCOOTER
SLEIGH
TANK
TOBOGGAN
TRAIN
VAN

TWISTED tip: HELICOPTER with an extra letter added will be 11 letters long, so should be easy to find.

28. CROSS WORDS

What's the TWIST?

Find each of the listed words in the grid.

Each entry in the grid is cross-shaped – either X or +. The letter at the centre of each cross-shape (E in this case) is used twice. All entries in the grid read horizontally from left to right for the first half of the word, then from top to bottom for the second half.

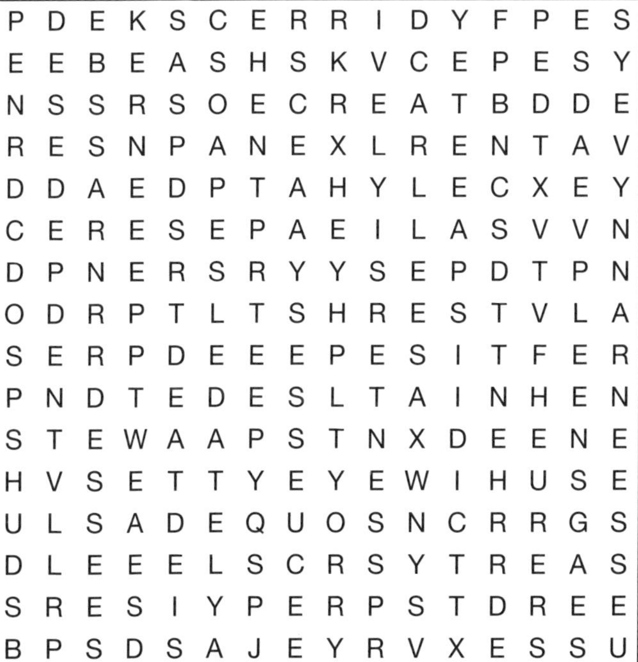

P	D	E	K	S	C	E	R	R	I	D	Y	F	P	E	S
E	E	B	E	A	S	H	S	K	V	C	E	P	E	S	Y
N	S	S	R	S	O	E	C	R	E	A	T	B	D	D	E
R	E	S	N	P	A	N	E	X	L	R	E	N	T	A	V
D	D	A	E	D	P	T	A	H	Y	L	E	C	X	E	Y
C	E	R	E	S	E	P	A	E	I	L	A	S	V	V	N
D	P	N	E	R	S	R	Y	Y	S	E	P	D	T	P	N
O	D	R	P	T	L	T	S	H	R	E	S	T	V	L	A
S	E	R	P	D	E	E	E	P	E	S	I	T	F	E	R
P	N	D	T	E	D	E	S	L	T	A	I	N	H	E	N
S	T	E	W	A	A	P	S	T	N	X	D	E	E	N	E
H	V	S	E	T	T	Y	E	Y	E	W	I	H	U	S	E
U	L	S	A	D	E	Q	U	O	S	N	C	R	R	G	S
D	L	E	E	E	L	S	C	R	S	Y	T	R	E	A	S
S	R	E	S	I	Y	P	E	R	P	S	T	D	R	E	E
B	P	S	D	S	A	J	E	Y	R	V	X	E	S	S	U

TWISTED tip: Divide each listed word in half, and search for one half at a time. This makes it easier to find the entry in the grid.

ADEQUATELY
BEAKER
BEEFED
BREATHLESS
CHEERINESS
COEXISTENT
CREATIVELY
DEADEN
DEGREE
EYEWITNESS
HEAVEN
JERSEY
PEELED
PREACHIEST
PREPOSSESS
PRETENDERS
SLEEPYHEAD
SLENDEREST
STEWARDESS
TREASURERS

29. EMPTY INSIDE

What's the TWIST?

Find each of the listed **types of puzzle** in the grid. They may be written forwards or backwards in any direction, including diagonally.

Fill in the 36 blank squares in the centre of the grid as you place the entries.

N	N	F	U	T	O	S	H	I	K	I	R	S	P	R	E
O	L	U	E	R	W	K	A	S	E	A	R	U	E	D	P
R	W	W	M	T	Y	Y	N	N	I	C	T	C	P	O	L
H	D	A	F	B	N	S	J	R	K	H	T	E	O	A	B
O	D	U	I	R	E	C	I	M	G	A	R	L	B	R	D
M	D	R	T	F							E	Y	I	L	F
W	I	R	W	S							R	D	R	E	U
N	O	E	O	N							G	I	N	K	U
C	S	R	R	W							E	C	O	G	S
O	A	O	D	E							E	D	S	A	E
B	A	T	T	L							U	A	I	E	O
O	D	T	R	H	A	S	O	I	K	C	A	H	S	T	N
L	E	S	T	S	R	D	J	R	L	P	W	R	O	I	I
E	R	I	E	S	C	R	D	A	C	M	B	N	R	W	M
O	L	E	C	O	H	U	C	E	F	R	R	I	T	D	O
S	M	A	R	G	A	N	A	R	R	O	W	W	O	R	D

ANAGRAMS
ARROW WORD
BATTLESHIPS
BRIDGES
CALCUDOKU
CROSSWORD
DOMINOES
FENCES
FITWORD
FUTOSHIKI
HANJIE
LABYRINTH
LIGHT UP
NUMBER LINK
RECTANGLES
SIMPLE LOOP
SKYSCRAPERS
SLITHERLINK
WORD LADDER
WORD SEARCH

TWISTED tip: Mark the entries you find in the grid lightly to avoid obscuring the letters you write in the central hole.

30. LITTLE CLUES

What's the TWIST?

The names of 20 **breeds of dog** are hidden in the grid. They may be written forwards or backwards in any direction, including diagonally.

Work out what the dog breeds are with the help of the initial letters given. The initials are listed alphabetically, which should help when there is more than one entry starting with the same letter.

G	O	D	P	E	E	H	S	A	T	H	B	E	O	N	S
U	P	D	R	S	E	E	N	A	D	T	A	E	R	G	C
A	R	O	N	E	H	L	A	L	L	R	N	N	U	O	H
U	L	V	M	U	X	I	D	U	A	S	S	N	S	D	N
H	E	R	E	E	O	O	H	O	E	B	G	G	N	L	A
A	I	T	E	S	R	H	B	T	O	D	R	O	E	L	U
U	N	R	O	T	R	A	X	P	Z	P	U	A	L	U	Z
H	A	N	N	E	R	H	N	O	A	U	B	E	D	B	E
I	P	E	A	S	O	I	R	I	F	S	S	S	N	O	R
H	S	T	I	E	A	U	E	E	A	S	E	H	U	M	R
C	R	E	T	L	E	N	O	V	U	N	T	O	O	S	B
E	E	R	A	D	E	R	B	R	E	K	T	O	H	K	E
S	K	R	M	P	F	T	K	E	H	R	K	B	Y	E	A
A	C	I	L	C	U	C	G	K	O	S	I	I	E	T	G
E	O	E	A	R	A	U	H	U	S	K	Y	H	R	U	L
B	C	R	D	J	H	G	R	E	T	T	E	S	G	O	E

TWISTED tip: The words have been chosen from amongst the most popular breeds of dog.

B..
B..
B..
C..
C......................S....................
D..
F..
G......................D....................
G..
H..
J......................R....................
L..
P..
P..
R..
S..
S..
S..
S..
T..

31. SHAPED WORDS

What's the TWIST?

Find each of the listed L-words in the grid.

Each entry in the grid is L-shaped, and may read either from top to bottom or bottom to top. The L-shapes are not rotated, but the upright stroke of the L is not always longer than the horizontal stroke. One entry is marked as an example.

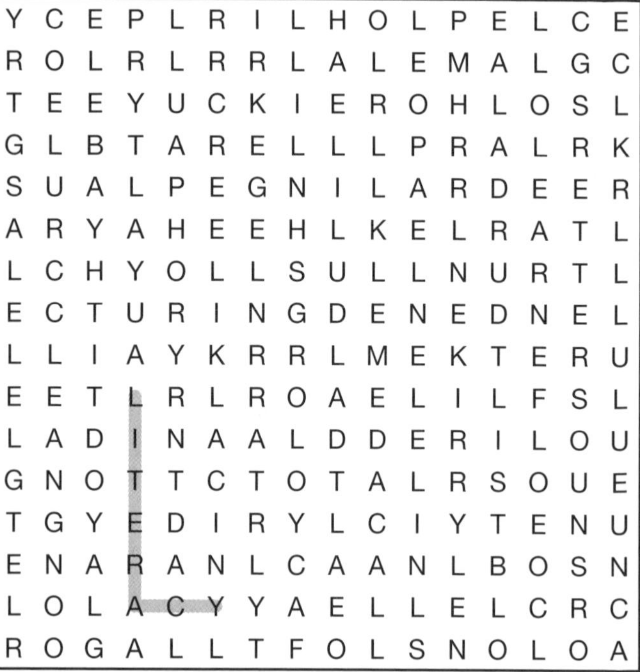

LABEL
LADDER
LAGOON
LAMP
LEAD
LEARNER
LECTURING
LEOPARD
LETTERS
LIKEN
LINGER
LISTEN
~~LITERACY~~
LOFTY
LONELY
LOYALTY
LUCKIER
LURCH
LUSH
LYRICAL

TWISTED tip: The L-shapes may be tall and thin or short and wide.

32. THIS AND THAT

What's the TWIST?

Find each of the listed missing words in the grid. They may be written forwards or backwards in any direction, including diagonally.

First complete each entry in the word list to make a well-known phrase. For example, RANTING AND .... completes as RANTING AND RAVING, so you must then search for RAVING in the grid.

N N I H N N E S W S I N L A D E
F R I W R S I N E R N N A L I E
E U P L T M A E A R O H L D N P
E W O E P I R G P N C N E U E O
P W L L U E E R I I E N G S E R
N E E W C N A H E E R G A R E I
A O G U I V L L R U N L O S E P
S R A V I D T U T R O I G G U E
T S W N E A S O R S E F H N O G
E G G G F A R G S W T G I S A C
F S R A E E R C R A T S G T E C
D A L L P D I I P O H L C A O L
L L P O R O T M N M I E W N D N
R N R P O E L I E E F E S N R R
E P I I O F O N L F O F R R R O
E R O A E N T U E M O H W S E E

TWISTED tip: The phrases in the word list are provided in alphabetical order of the first word, so the missing words are not given in alphabetical order.

BUSINESS AND ....
BY AND ....
CAUSE AND ....
CHEESE AND ....
CLOAK AND ....
CRIME AND ....
CUP AND ....
HIGH AND ....
PRIM AND ....
PROFIT AND ....
PROS AND ....
PURE AND ....
RAIN AND ....
RANTING AND ....
READ AND ....
RIGHT AND ....
RISE AND ....
SALT AND ....
SUIT AND ....
TOSSED AND ....

33. WRAPAROUND

What's the TWIST?

Find each of the listed **monetary currencies** in the grid. They may be written forwards or backwards in any direction, including diagonally.

Entries can wrap around from one edge of the grid to the other, so imagine that the grid repeats immediately on all sides. Words that wrap around continue on the opposite side to correspond with where they would be on the repeated grid.

O O R C E R Z T U L A I D E W U
H O A S A A A L I A O O O P T A
Y Z O E O O A Z I A K L D R Z L
C O O P A A S O P U A W Y R B U
U D B E L R Z C R N D A O S A R
O A R O M D Y R O N D F A N K M
H Y I P I L O L N N P U U A N C
A C E N L I O R D N S K N U G T
F R A N C E R N R A Y T U H L B
Y R D R O E I P C A N W A A B H
I T B A D R D U T H A A L N D A
O R O L O N K L U K O O R O P L
L U I L U U Y O L H N Y D I A T
R U F O Z A I O H O L K N F A R
G A P D E N E T K O N C O W F D
U R N U N P U R A N A S A E F L

BAHT
DINAR
DOLLAR
DRACHMA
DRAM
ESCUDO
EURO
FLORIN
FRANC
GUILDER
KRONE
KUNA
KYAT
LIRA
PESO
POUND
WON
YEN
YUAN
ZLOTY

TWISTED tip: Many of the entries in this grid overlap.

34. LEFTOVER LETTERS

What's the TWIST?

Find each of the listed **types of sport** in the grid. They may be written forwards or backwards in any direction, including diagonally.

Each entry in the grid includes one extra letter (not shown in the word list). Make a note of the extra letter beside the corresponding sport in the list. Then use the letters to spell out a related phrase in the space at the bottom of the page.

F	S	A	I	R	N	L	S	S	E	O	I	N	G	G	L
E	B	V	N	S	E	A	M	M	I	J	G	N	L	T	T
N	S	T	R	G	I	R	U	R	N	N	I	N	G	G	I
C	I	N	R	C	F	L	H	G	I	V	S	N	G	N	L
L	U	V	L	F	U	O	L	W	L	O	I	N	L	B	O
I	N	I	N	L	N	A	O	I	W	L	O	L	N	J	L
N	N	C	W	C	A	O	D	I	A	H	A	B	U	W	L
G	E	B	K	D	R	B	M	C	T	B	I	Y	D	Y	I
Y	T	E	I	U	O	M	Y	N	T	B	D	P	G	T	C
I	Y	A	G	X	I	C	I	E	E	O	A	N	N	R	T
A	I	B	B	N	N	M	K	R	R	I	L	L	A	E	A
B	U	I	G	Y	D	S	G	G	P	L	A	F	L	H	K
Y	N	I	C	A	A	M	S	I	O	G	L	L	L	C	U
G	O	L	B	E	I	L	C	L	L	S	M	O	I	R	R
O	C	C	B	Y	O	H	N	W	O	O	N	B	V	A	N
V	U	E	C	G	U	I	W	G	K	O	A	B	K	W	B

TWISTED tip: The X in BOXING is an unusual letter, so look for it first.

ARCHERY
BADMINTON
BASKETBALL
BOXING
CYCLING
DIVING
FENCING

FOOTBALL
GOLF
HANDBALL
HOCKEY
JUDO
ROWING
RUGBY

RUNNING
SAILING
SWIMMING
TENNIS
VOLLEYBALL
WATER POLO

....

35. SECRET WORDS

What's the TWIST?

Find each of the listed words and phrases in the grid. They may be written forwards or backwards in any direction, including diagonally.

Each entry in the word list contains at least one concealed **colour**; for example SCARED contains a hidden RED. Delete the hidden colours from the words and phrases when searching for them in the grid. So for SCARED search for SCA.

TWISTED tip: Only two entries contain the standard colours of the rainbow. You'll need to think creatively to work out the rest!

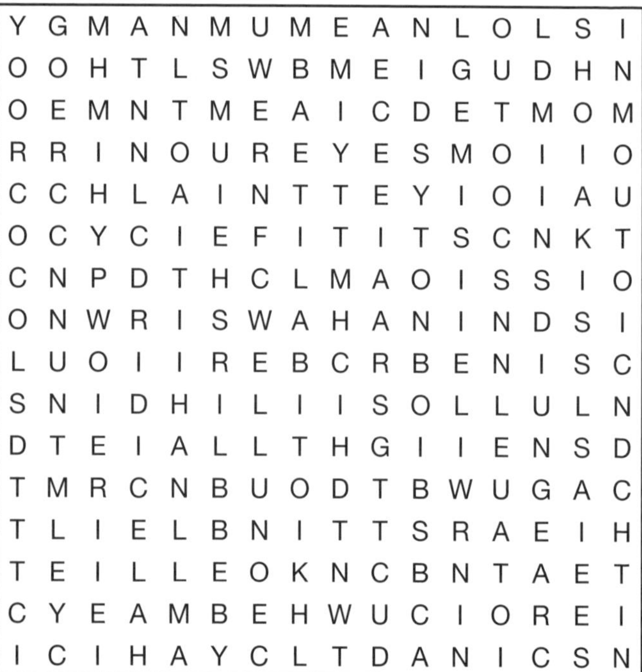

Y	G	M	A	N	M	U	M	E	A	N	L	O	L	S	I
O	O	H	T	L	S	W	B	M	E	I	G	U	D	H	N
O	E	M	N	T	M	E	A	I	C	D	E	T	M	O	M
R	R	I	N	O	U	R	E	Y	E	S	M	O	I	I	O
C	C	H	L	A	I	N	T	T	E	Y	I	O	I	A	U
O	C	Y	C	I	E	F	I	T	I	T	S	C	N	K	T
C	N	P	D	T	H	C	L	M	A	O	I	S	S	I	O
O	N	W	R	I	S	W	A	H	A	N	I	N	D	S	I
L	U	O	I	I	R	E	B	C	R	B	E	N	I	S	C
S	N	I	D	H	I	L	I	I	S	O	L	L	U	L	N
D	T	E	I	A	L	L	T	H	G	I	I	E	N	S	D
T	M	R	C	N	B	U	O	D	T	B	W	U	G	A	C
T	L	I	E	L	B	N	I	T	T	S	R	A	E	I	H
T	E	I	L	L	E	O	K	N	C	B	N	T	A	E	T
C	Y	E	A	M	B	E	H	W	U	C	I	O	R	E	I
I	C	I	H	A	Y	C	L	T	D	A	N	I	C	S	N

BADMINTON
CAMBERWELL
CHAMBERLAIN
CONSTANT
CRUSTACEAN
CYANIDE
DISCREDITED
FASHION
LEGISLATE
LITTLE MONKEY
MARIGOLD
MOROSELY
NOM DE PLUME
PRICE RISE
RUB YOUR EYES
SCARED
STEALTHIEST
TEALIGHT
UNIMPEACHABLE
WHISKY

36. WARPED VISION

What's the TWIST?

Find each of the listed **types of cocktail** in the grid. They may be written forwards or backwards in any direction, including diagonally.

The rows and columns that make up the grid have been twisted, but you should still solve the puzzle as if they were perfectly straight.

TWISTED tip: Try starting with the edges of the grid, where the lines are straighter.

BELLINI
BLACK VELVET
BLOODHOUND
BLOODY MARY
DAIQUIRI
HAVANA COOLER
HURRICANE
MAI TAI
MANHATTAN
MARGARITA
MOJITO
PANAMA
PARADISE
PINK GIN
PINK LADY
SCREWDRIVER
SIDECAR
SNOWBALL
TEQUILA SUNRISE
WHITE RUSSIAN

37. LEFTOVER LETTERS

What's the TWIST?

Find each of the listed **types of mammal** in the grid. They may be written forwards or backwards in any direction, including diagonally.

Each entry in the grid includes one extra letter (not shown in the word list). Make a note of the extra letter beside the corresponding animal in the list. Then use the letters to spell out a related phrase in the space at the bottom of the page.

H	Q	L	E	M	S	O	L	O	O	H	H	C	U	D	I
E	O	E	O	M	Y	S	T	H	W	E	W	N	E	R	E
I	O	R	P	N	M	H	O	R	S	O	O	E	O	H	U
R	H	P	S	N	T	R	A	M	E	A	E	A	I	E	U
O	E	D	C	H	A	T	H	R	F	G	I	P	O	T	E
D	S	L	A	H	E	S	E	L	R	L	P	O	A	H	E
E	E	L	X	B	E	E	E	R	M	O	O	B	M	O	M
N	O	E	R	O	X	M	E	L	P	D	M	O	L	H	I
T	O	R	E	E	A	O	I	P	F	O	U	S	W	U	N
F	N	R	I	R	G	N	O	N	M	I	M	R	T	P	A
G	N	R	G	I	O	T	A	W	S	D	P	R	H	O	K
L	G	I	T	N	A	K	H	E	R	A	O	A	E	O	T
E	T	U	H	M	M	E	S	O	Y	I	O	R	C	L	O
P	R	Q	U	R	T	Y	E	C	I	H	T	E	H	O	O
M	E	S	M	A	O	G	G	R	E	O	O	O	R	R	E
E	O	A	W	P	E	R	E	O	T	P	Q	T	A	O	T

BEAR
CAT
COW
DEER
DOG
FOX
HIPPOPOTAMUS
HORSE
HYENA
LION
MONKEY
MOUSE
OTTER
PIG
SEAL
SHEEP
SQUIRREL
TIGER
WOLF
WOMBAT

TWISTED tip: The hidden phrase relates to a large, well-known mammal that isn't in the word list.

38. SYMBOLIC

What's the TWIST?

Find each of the listed words and phrases in the grid. They may be written forwards or backwards in any direction, including diagonally.

All occurrences of MIN and MAX in the listed words and phrases have been replaced by < or > respectively in the grid. So for ABDOMINAL search for ABDO<AL.

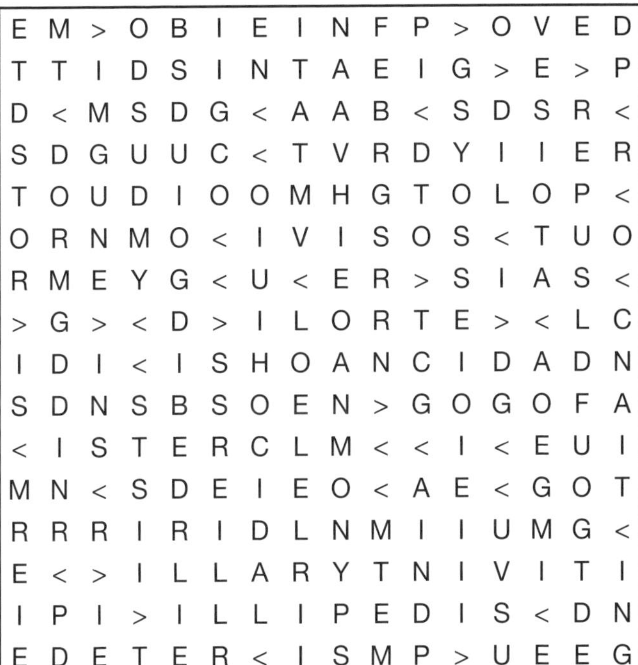

E M > O B I E I N F P > O V E D
T T I D S I N T A E I G > E > P
D < M S D G < A A B < S D S R <
S D G U U C < T V R D Y I I E R
T O U D I O O M H G T O L O P <
O R N M O < I V I S O S < T U O
R M E Y G < U < E R > S I A S <
> G > < D > I L O R T E > < L C
I D I < I S H O A N C I D A D N
S D N S B S O E N > G O G O F A
< I S T E R C L M < < I < E U I
M N < S D E I E O < A E < G O T
R R R I R I D L N M I I U M G <
E < > I L L A R Y T N I V I T I
I P I > I L L I P E D I S < D N
E D E T E R < I S M P > U E E G

ABDOMINAL
ADMINISTRATE
ALUMINIUM
DETERMINISM
DEVOMAX
DIMINISH
DOMINION
FEMININE
IGNOMINIOUS
MAXED OUT
MAXILLARY
MAXILLIPED
MAXIM GUN
MINING
MINISTER
OVERCOMING
REMINISCENT
STORM AXIS
SUPERMAX
TRIMMINGS

TWISTED tip: Not all of the < and > symbols in the grid are necessarily used by word entries.

39. CROSS WORDS

What's the TWIST?

Find each of the listed words and phrases in the grid.

Each entry in the grid is cross-shaped – either **X** or **+**. The letter at the centre of each cross-shape (C in this case) is used twice. All entries in the grid read horizontally from left to right for the first half of the word or phrase, then from top to bottom for the second half.

E	O	L	A	A	C	B	P	H	U	C	S	T	I	I	H
E	K	R	A	N	D	C	S	O	P	U	A	A	T	S	O
A	Y	O	K	N	C	T	R	A	C	R	E	C	E	P	E
R	E	C	I	P	I	E	H	O	L	U	A	L	I	A	C
E	A	A	A	A	R	C	H	I	M	L	S	E	E	D	C
H	C	L	T	B	E	T	A	N	C	I	A	H	E	B	S
A	L	S	R	M	C	S	I	L	R	F	C	A	E	I	S
C	K	I	U	Y	C	M	C	C	E	L	I	A	R	A	H
M	I	S	C	O	N	S	N	I	A	C	E	C	L	C	C
L	S	N	T	A	S	U	T	E	S	L	A	E	E	E	N
S	E	U	E	N	L	P	L	N	A	S	H	S	S	D	T
E	L	F	D	D	E	A	O	N	C	N	E	U	O	O	H
N	N	I	I	B	A	C	K	S	F	A	C	T	C	S	U
M	I	C	R	O	E	E	T	C	T	E	K	E	O	R	L
C	N	H	E	R	C	S	L	S	R	O	S	A	S	C	O
I	C	E	C	S	E	T	T	C	A	C	R	S	O	H	K

ALCHEMICAL
ARCHITECTS
BACKSPACES
ENCYCLICAL
FACT-CHECKS
HACKNEY CAB
HOCUS-POCUS
INCIDENCES
LACTIC ACID
MECHANICAL
MICROFICHE
MISCONSTRUCTED
O'CLOCK
RECEPTACLE
RECIPROCAL
RECONNECTS
RECUSANCES
SACRIFICED
SCORCH
UNCRITICAL

TWISTED tip: The words in this puzzle are all quite long, so it is likely that many of them will share letters in the grid.

40. SECRET WORDS

What's the TWIST?

Find each of the listed words and phrases in the grid. They may be written forwards or backwards in any direction, including diagonally.

Each entry in the word list contains at least one concealed **musical instrument**; for example SHARPEN contains a hidden HARP. Delete the hidden instruments from the words and phrases when searching for them in the grid. So for SHARPEN search for SEN.

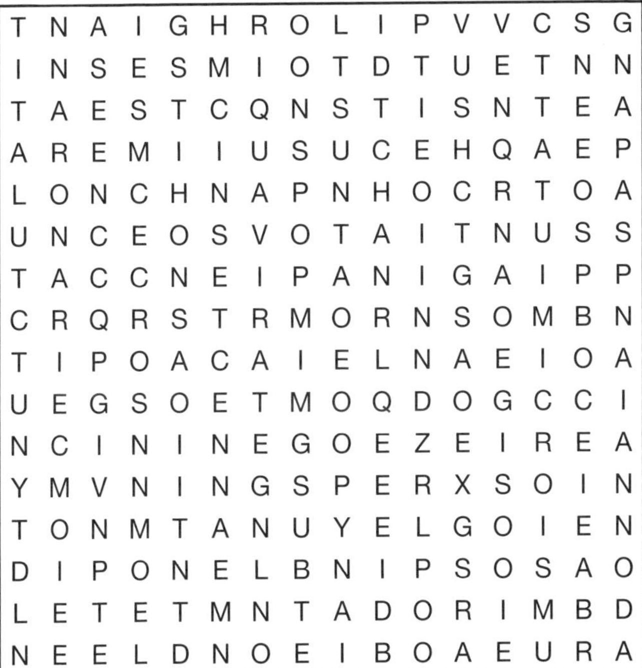

TWISTED tip: Different varieties of musical instrument have been concealed, from wind to percussion.

ABSOLUTE
BELLADONNA
BELLIGERENT
CHANCELLOR
CONUNDRUM
CONVOLUTED
DEPOSITARY
EARLY RETIREMENT
EMBELLISHMENT
HARPOON GUN
INORGANIC
INTUBATION
INVIOLABLE
LABELLING
MICROORGANISM
NECESSITARIAN
ORGANISATION
POLLUTED
QUADRUMVIRATE
SHARPEN

41. WRAPAROUND

What's the TWIST?

Find each of the listed **rivers** in the grid. They may be written forwards or backwards in any direction, including diagonally.

Entries can wrap around from one edge of the grid to the other, so imagine that the grid repeats immediately on all sides. Names of rivers that wrap around continue on the opposite side to correspond with where they would be on the repeated grid.

S E R E I I U V G U A E D N E M
N D R I A H A U L A G O P D V U
A S N V R R D A O S U R A L A U
L L G N D R O L V R S O O N N S
E N N N E R N H O D P I U T O L
E U N T D U L S C A R N U I I R
V N N E L T U V S E N R P H R S
N R E P R T I M T I P S D A R E
E E R E S N L S M S I G A S N V
D N M T E A E E D A C N A E E Z
L N E A I I U B E D E A P A P E
A A E E N S A U D V E N E A B U
E O G D E A Z N D I H L O V A R
U L A L R D I A O L M A I V S U
N O B N V E A D U E I S A U R I
O E V I P N S A A A T U D E N O

DANUBE
DNIEPER
DNIESTER
DOURO
DRAVA
ELBE
GUADIANA
LOIRE
MEUSE
NEMAN
ODER
PECHORA
PRUT
RHINE
SEINE
TAGUS
TISZA
URAL
VISTULA
VOLGA

TWISTED tip: Start with the longest words as they are easiest to find.

42. EMPTY INSIDE

What's the TWIST?

Find each of the listed **types of cloud** in the grid. They may be written forwards or backwards in any direction, including diagonally.

Fill in the 36 blank squares in the centre of the grid as you place the entries.

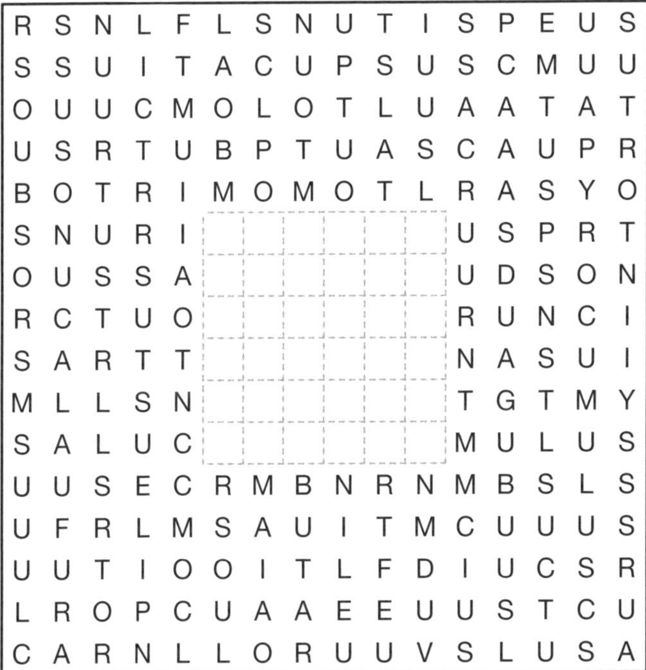

ALTOCUMULUS
ALTOSTRATUS
CASTELLANUS
CIRROCUMULUS
CIRROSTRATUS
CIRRUS
CUMULOGENITUS
CUMULONIMBUS
FIBRATUS
INCUS
INTORTUS
LACUNOSUS
NIMBOSTRATUS
OPACUS
PILEUS
PYROCUMULUS
STRATIFORMIS
UNCINUS
UNDULATUS
VELUM

TWISTED tip: Write the missing letters into the grid in pencil in case you make a mistake.

43. LEFTOVER LETTERS

What's the TWIST?

Find each of the listed **leading actors** in the grid. They may be written forwards or backwards in any direction, including diagonally.

Each entry in the grid includes one extra letter (not shown in the word list). Make a note of the extra letter beside the corresponding name in the list. Then use the letters to spell out a related phrase in the space at the bottom of the page.

ANDREWS
BOGART
BRANDO
CRAWFORD
DE NIRO
FISHER
FONDA
HEPBURN
HOFFMAN
KEATON
KELLY
LEMMON
MONROE
NEWMAN
OLIVIER
SARANDON
STEWART
STREEP
TAYLOR
WASHINGTON

TWISTED tip: The hidden phrase describes something actors might be inclined to do.

....

44. LITTLE CLUES

What's the TWIST?

The names of 20 **breakfast foods and drinks** are hidden in the grid. They may be written forwards or backwards in any direction, including diagonally.

Work out what the words and phrases are with the help of the initial letters given. The initials are listed alphabetically, which should help when there is more than one entry starting with the same letter.

G N I D D U P K C A L B S I A U
M S B C E B E T I F H N D U B O
M U O O E G L A R K A T O U C O
A E S O I A A U E E B A E R E A
T P G H E L I S B I N L E E O G
O M P R R T E D U O I O G C N G
A E E L S O E D C A P C L I N E
S C E A E K O A E B S O G U W D
T A L F A J B M S G N H O J O E
C A R B G C U T A C G C M E R I
D E P A S T R I E S E U E G B R
D A I N L C H P C U N A L N H F
U O T A M O T G A E T N E A S U
P R T N A S S I O R C I T R A B
P A N C A K E S S D P A T O H N
G G E D E H C A O P G P E G T A

A..................J..................
B......................................
B..................B..................
B..................P..................
B..................E..................
C......................................
C......................................

F..................E..................
F..................S..................
H..................B..................
M......................................
O......................................
O..................J..................
P...........A...........C...........

P......................................
P......................................
P..................E..................
S......................................
T......................................
T......................................

TWISTED tip: The entries with multiple initials should be the easiest to guess.

45. SECRET WORDS

What's the TWIST?

Find each of the listed words and phrases in the grid. They may be written forwards or backwards in any direction, including diagonally.

Each entry in the word list contains at least one concealed **tree**; for example WHIPLASH contains a hidden ASH. Delete the hidden trees from the words and phrases when searching for them in the grid. So for WHIPLASH search for WHIPL.

V	W	B	D	E	S	M	T	V	M	T	E	M	R	R	D
E	C	E	E	D	E	A	E	B	Y	R	A	M	N	I	N
X	S	M	A	R	G	R	A	L	I	N	G	N	U	A	E
O	O	O	O	O	U	L	H	N	W	R	E	V	T	D	A
T	R	W	A	O	I	T	E	I	T	N	E	S	S	B	P
N	E	C	O	A	R	E	C	N	A	A	N	D	D	E	E
L	C	I	O	O	P	L	G	E	O	E	R	A	W	A	I
L	N	G	V	L	D	A	C	E	T	T	U	Y	W	I	N
N	A	A	E	I	R	N	N	E	S	I	I	S	S	M	A
O	I	W	R	N	V	C	A	C	N	R	A	N	S	S	L
E	D	F	W	N	A	E	W	A	E	O	B	V	P	P	M
A	L	E	H	F	A	C	E	H	O	S	I	E	A	H	T
A	L	I	I	R	A	A	U	N	I	F	N	E	H	N	E
H	O	E	N	N	T	N	E	A	A	P	E	A	B	L	E
C	N	S	G	A	H	T	R	D	R	X	L	R	R	P	C
E	E	L	M	I	D	F	I	S	A	A	L	L	D	U	P

ALIMENTARY
ALL SPRUCED UP
APPEARANCES
BALDERDASHES
BAYONET
CLOAKROOM
DIANA SPENCER
EXOPLANET
EYEWITNESS
FACEPALM
GRACE DARLING
HAPPINESS
HAZELNUTS
HOLLYWOOD
INFIRMARY
MIDFIELDERS
NAVAL ARCHITECTURE
OVERWHELMING
WILLOW WARE
WHIPLASH

TWISTED tip: You don't need to know lots of types of tree to complete this puzzle; if you find the words in the grid you can work out what's missing from them.

46. SHAPED WORDS

What's the TWIST?

Find each of the listed **precious stone** themed words and phrases in the grid.

Each entry in the grid is found in the shape of a diamond, always reading clockwise and starting from one of the four corners. One entry is marked as an example.

TWISTED tip: All diamond shapes in the grid have three sides of the same length and one less letter on the fourth side.

AMETHYST
BRACELET
CABOCHON
CUFFLINK
EARRINGS
EMERALDS
GOLD
HAIRPINS
HELENITE
JADE
~~MOHS' HARDNESS~~
NECKLACE
OBSIDIAN
OPAL
PENDANTS
PERIDOTS
RED BERYL
RING
RUBY
SAPPHIRE

47. WRAPAROUND

What's the TWIST?

Find each of the listed **paper** themed words and phrases in the grid. They may be written forwards or backwards in any direction, including diagonally.

Entries can wrap around from one edge of the grid to the other, so imagine that the grid repeats immediately on all sides. Words and phrases that wrap around continue on the opposite side to correspond with where they would be on the repeated grid.

TWISTED tip: Short entries that wrap around can be very hard to find – leave these for last.

ARCHITECTURAL
ATLAS
BRIEF
CROWN
EXECUTIVE
FANFOLD
FOOLSCAP
IMPERIAL
LEDGER
LEGAL
LETTER
MEDIUM
OCTAVO
ORIGAMI
QUARTO
ROYAL
SHEET
SMALL POST
SUPER
TABLOID

48. EMPTY INSIDE

What's the TWIST?

Find each of the listed **mistake** themed words and phrases in the grid. They may be written forwards or backwards in any direction, including diagonally.

Fill in the 36 blank squares in the centre of the grid as you place the entries.

N	D	D	T	O	I	L	E	R	O	S	O	E	R	A	L
I	T	F	I	D	M	P	S	S	T	A	L	L	E	D	E
E	M	A	S	A	E	I	E	T	M	O	D	N	O	K	I
I	R	I	O	D	L	L	S	E	E	E	T	O	S	O	U
U	D	L	I	O	E	S	L	P	B	O	T	T	F	S	L
T	I	U	E	S							E	I	E	I	E
A	T	R	O	S							E	T	A	S	A
I	D	E	K	O							C	S	A	I	F
S	H	T	W	O							R	E	T	L	T
P	T	N	K	M							S	R	D	E	O
I	C	P	D	N							E	I	E	T	W
I	E	L	U	S	M	T	T	V	L	T	H	N	E	E	I
L	L	L	I	B	O	O	S	S	U	I	I	T	E	H	B
O	B	M	L	U	O	I	U	R	A	O	P	M	S	R	E
L	O	E	T	K	M	P	U	S	F	S	O	U	O	L	S
N	S	I	U	D	D	L	L	R	W	L	I	F	P	B	F

BLUNDER
DEBACLE
ERROR
FAILURE
FAULT
FIASCO
LEFT OUT
LET SLIP
MELTDOWN
MISLAID
MISPLACED
MISTOOK
MISUNDERSTOOD
NEGLECTED
OMITTED
OVERLOOKED
OVERSIGHT
SHAMBLES
SLIP-UP
STALLED

TWISTED tip: Every letter in the puzzle's empty heart is part of a listed word, which means that most entries will be found around the centre of the grid.

49. SYMBOLIC

What's the TWIST?

Find each of the listed words and phrases in the grid. They may be written forwards or backwards in any direction, including diagonally.

All names of playing card suits (hearts, diamonds, spades and clubs) in the listed words and phrases have been replaced by the corresponding suit symbol in the grid. So for BROKEN HEART search for BROKEN ♥.

♥	O	R	N	U	K	C	A	T	T	A	♥	I	G	N	A
♦	N	W	♦	C	♥	F	O	E	G	N	A	H	C	S	O
K	I	G	♥	R	E	G	G	N	I	R	♦	N	♠	F	H
T	G	♠	N	E	D	R	A	G	♥	U	E	N	N	B	G
♣	H	D	F	H	O	D	I	C	E	O	I	E	L	O	U
S	T	O	H	T	H	G	O	♠	G	T	♥	O	R	B	O
A	♣	H	E	E	I	B	F	T	I	T	O	H	C	R	R
N	T	A	E	G	R	O	U	E	H	D	T	N	N	O	E
D	Z	T	E	O	O	N	V	C	♦	E	F	♠	T	K	H
W	O	A	T	T	S	A	C	B	K	I	♠	O	A	E	T
I	Q	I	T	♣	H	K	E	T	N	E	I	W	C	N	N
C	♣	O	A	E	C	B	O	O	K	♣	T	N	O	♥	I
H	A	B	N	A	♥	A	D	H	H	B	♠	A	H	R	♦
D	S	I	B	F	A	I	N	T	♥	E	D	K	N	R	K
O	M	♦	♠	S	T	A	T	E	O	F	T	♥	♣	D	♣
♦	H	I	♠	♠	A	♠	A	L	L	A	C	D	T	W	♠

TWISTED tip: As with the letters in a standard word search, the symbols do not rotate to match the direction in which words are placed in the grid.

BLOOD DIAMOND
BOOK CLUB
BROKEN HEART
BUCKET AND SPADE
CALL A SPADE A SPADE
CHANGE OF HEART
CLUB SANDWICH
CLUB TOGETHER
DIAMONDBACK
DIAMOND IN THE ROUGH
DIAMOND MINE
DIAMOND RING
DO THE SPADEWORK
FAINT-HEARTED
GARDEN SPADE
HAVE IT IN SPADES
HEART ATTACK
NIGHTCLUB
SPADEFOOT TOAD
STATE OF THE ART

50. WARPED VISION

What's the TWIST?

Find each of the listed **arts and crafts** themed words and phrases in the grid. They may be written forwards or backwards in any direction, including diagonally.

The rows and columns that make up the grid have been twisted, but you should still solve the puzzle as if they were perfectly straight.

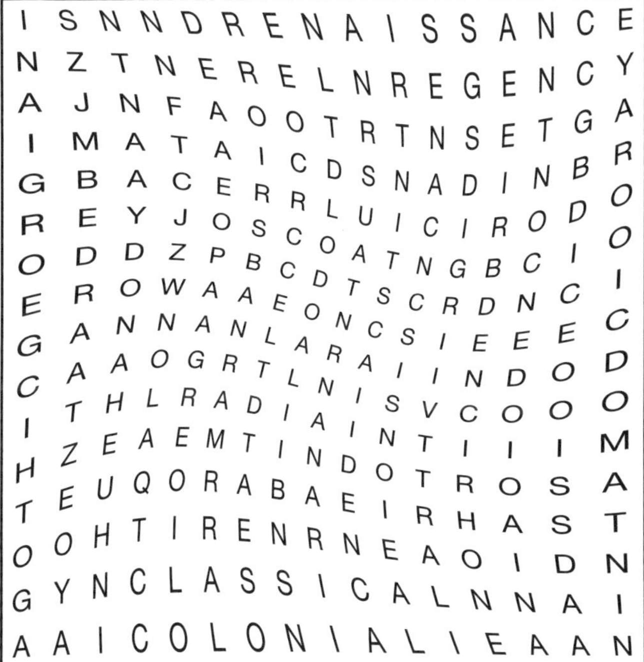

TWISTED tip: Try drawing on feint grid lines to make it easier to follow the rows and columns.

ARTS AND CRAFTS
BAROQUE
BYZANTINE
CLASSICAL
COLONIAL
CORINTHIAN
DORIC
EDWARDIAN
GEORGIAN
GOTHIC
IONIC
JACOBEAN
MODERNIST
NEOCLASSICIST
NORMAN
PALLADIAN
REGENCY
RENAISSANCE
TUDOR
VICTORIAN

51. LEFTOVER LETTERS

What's the TWIST?

Find each of the listed **meat** themed words and phrases in the grid. They may be written forwards or backwards in any direction, including diagonally.

Each entry in the grid includes one extra letter (not shown in the word list). Make a note of the extra letter beside the corresponding word or phrase in the list. Then use the letters to spell out a related phrase in the space at the bottom of the page.

I	B	K	C	A	O	E	L	C	H	A	H	R	S	H	V
G	B	K	K	H	O	C	G	T	M	H	S	M	N	A	T
A	V	T	P	R	R	N	H	U	G	N	O	E	U	E	I
B	E	C	P	H	T	I	M	R	A	O	B	P	H	L	M
B	C	H	M	A	B	G	C	A	N	S	N	Y	O	G	A
N	S	K	A	R	K	M	G	K	S	O	W	O	D	L	B
L	B	F	B	T	G	E	M	E	E	I	T	G	S	R	S
U	E	A	B	A	F	N	G	Y	L	N	P	H	K	E	L
L	L	O	H	E	E	A	R	D	M	E	C	C	T	N	B
E	K	C	S	O	E	T	N	A	O	V	U	H	K	U	T
I	A	S	V	S	U	B	S	R	C	I	G	H	B	I	M
S	C	R	U	M	O	A	K	E	D	O	R	I	B	E	H
R	V	A	G	A	E	L	A	N	S	K	A	T	Y	E	B
O	S	A	R	H	A	L	N	N	N	M	B	O	R	A	U
S	N	A	P	S	E	S	H	A	L	A	M	I	B	A	R
K	S	A	V	H	A	E	L	G	R	V	M	H	M	L	P

BEEF
CHICKEN
DUCK
GOOSE
HAM
LAMB
MEATBALLS
MINCE
MUTTON
PARTRIDGE
PHEASANT
PORK
RABBIT
SALAMI
SAUSAGES
STEAK
TURKEY
VEAL
VENISON
WILD BOAR

TWISTED tip: Most of the entries are clustered around the centre of the puzzle.

....

52. SECRET WORDS

What's the TWIST?

Find each of the listed words and phrases in the grid. They may be written forwards or backwards in any direction, including diagonally.

Each entry in the word list contains at least one concealed **country**; for example ASSYRIAN contains a hidden SYRIA. Delete the hidden countries from the words and phrases when searching for them in the grid. So for ASSYRIAN search for ASN.

ABNORMALITY
ANTIPERSPIRANT
AS PER USUAL
ASSYRIAN
BACALAOS
BENJAMIN DISRAELI
BIBLIOMANIA
CANE PALM
CHICKEN YARD
CRINIGEROUS
DEGREE CELSIUS
GLOSS PAINT
HELMETED GUINEAFOWL
HONEST-TO-GOD
INCUBATOR
MACHINATIONS
NORMAL TAX
PANGOLA GRASS
VAGABOND
WITH MUCH ADO

TWISTED tip: Starting with the longest words or phrases rapidly reduces the remaining space in the grid, making other entries easier to spot.

53. SHAPED WORDS

What's the TWIST?

Find each of the listed **London Underground stations** in the grid.

Each entry in the grid is found in the shape of a letter U. Entries may be read in either direction along the body of the U and the U-shapes are never rotated. One entry is marked as an example.

R U B Y P B O C O W O N E N S P
G P N E L X O R P A T E W E I T
N I P P O D L R E T E A S D K O
M R I H Q I D S T R E K U O C T
A K A C U E E N S P A R K N N R
R W L R D R Y O C B R L S C O U
B L E A O L L I S H I L T T E Y
R S N N G E E N R I I E E S L E
P E O E L N Y T R G T N N E K S
A B T S N O T I N H B A R X L D
D D I N G T I R K E S L S E S H
H L N L R O W E R H I L O A I U
G E K H E E N P A W H T U I H D
D A I L B U R L P A A A E P K T
A O R W O R U R I N U D N E T I
P P M B C O I S L S A R K R L H

ANGEL
BOW ROAD
CROXLEY
DOLLIS HILL
~~EARL'S COURT~~
EPPING
GREEN PARK
HIGH BARNET
KILBURN
LEYTONSTONE
MARBLE ARCH
NEASDEN
OLD STREET
PADDINGTON
QUEEN'S PARK
RUISLIP
SOUTHWARK
TOWER HILL
UPNEY
WATERLOO

TWISTED tip: The middle section of the U-shape is always at least three letters wide, and corresponds with the middle of the word, so may be easiest to find first.

54. LEFTOVER LETTERS

What's the TWIST?

Find each of the listed **disagreement** themed words and phrases in the grid. They may be written forwards or backwards in any direction, including diagonally.

Each entry in the grid includes one extra letter (not shown in the word list). Make a note of the extra letter beside the corresponding word or phrase in the list. Then use the letters to spell out a related phrase in the space at the bottom of the page.

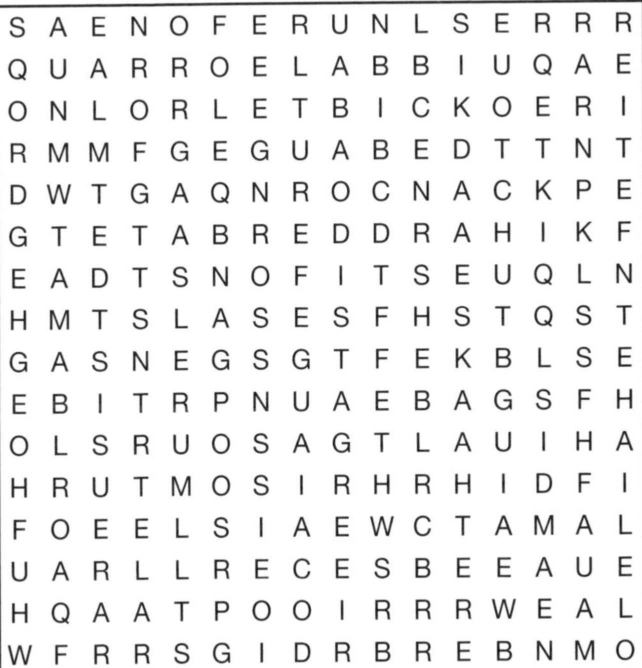

S	A	E	N	O	F	E	R	U	N	L	S	E	R	R	R
Q	U	A	R	R	O	E	L	A	B	B	I	U	Q	A	E
O	N	L	O	R	L	E	T	B	I	C	K	O	E	R	I
R	M	M	F	G	E	G	U	A	B	E	D	T	T	N	T
D	W	T	G	A	Q	N	R	O	C	N	A	C	K	P	E
G	T	E	T	A	B	R	E	D	D	R	A	H	I	K	F
E	A	D	T	S	N	O	F	I	T	S	E	U	Q	L	N
H	M	T	S	L	A	S	E	S	F	H	S	T	Q	S	T
G	A	S	N	E	G	S	G	T	F	E	K	B	L	S	E
E	B	I	T	R	P	N	U	A	E	B	A	G	S	F	H
O	L	S	R	U	O	S	A	G	T	L	A	U	I	H	A
H	R	U	T	M	O	S	I	R	H	R	H	I	D	F	I
F	O	E	E	L	S	I	A	E	W	C	T	A	M	A	L
U	A	R	L	L	R	E	C	E	S	B	E	E	A	U	E
H	Q	A	A	T	P	O	O	I	R	R	R	W	E	A	L
W	F	R	R	S	G	I	D	R	B	R	E	B	N	M	O

ALTERCATE
BICKER
DEBATE
DISAGREE
DISCUSS
DISPUTE
FALL OUT
FEUD
FIGHT
HAGGLE
QUARREL
QUESTION
QUIBBLE
REASON
REMONSTRATE
RESIST
ROW
SPAR
SQUABBLE
WRANGLE

TWISTED tip: Searching for the words in the order listed could help you to guess the hidden phrase earlier.

55. SYMBOLIC

What's the TWIST?

Find each of the listed words in the grid. They may be written forwards or backwards in any direction, including diagonally.

All occurrences of AND in the listed words have been replaced by an ampersand symbol (&) in the grid. So for GLANDULAR search for GL&ULAR.

TWISTED tip: Try deleting the AND from each word and just searching for the rest of the word in the grid, using the & symbol purely for checking.

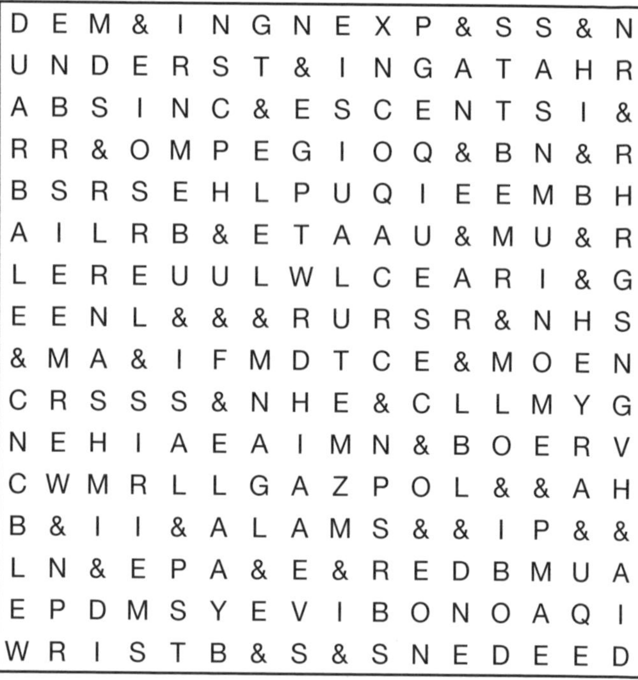

ABANDONED
BANDAGES
CANDELABRA
DEMANDING
EXPANDS
GLANDULAR
HANDSTAND
INCANDESCENT
LANDSCAPE
MANDARIN
NEANDERTHAL
OUTLANDISH
PANDEMONIUM
QUANDARY
RANDOM
SALAMANDER
UNDERSTANDING
VANDALISM
WRISTBAND
ZINFANDEL

56. LEFTOVER LETTERS

What's the TWIST?

Find each of the listed **fictional villains** in the grid. They may be written forwards or backwards in any direction, including diagonally.

Each entry in the grid includes one extra letter (not shown in the word list). Make a note of the extra letter beside the corresponding name in the list. Then use the letters to spell out a related phrase in the space at the bottom of the page.

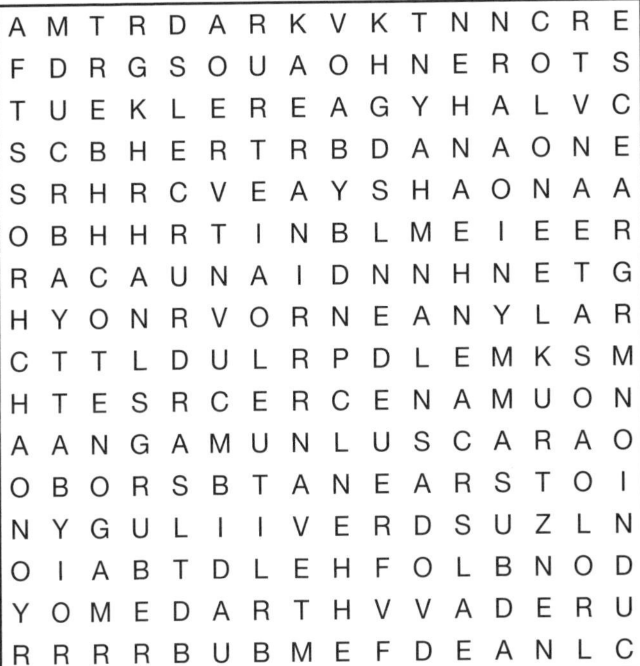

A	M	T	R	D	A	R	K	V	K	T	N	N	C	R	E
F	D	R	G	S	O	U	A	O	H	N	E	R	O	T	S
T	U	E	K	L	E	R	E	A	G	Y	H	A	L	V	C
S	C	B	H	E	R	T	R	B	D	A	N	A	O	N	E
S	R	H	R	C	V	E	A	Y	S	H	A	O	N	A	A
O	B	H	H	R	T	I	N	B	L	M	E	I	E	E	R
R	A	C	A	U	N	A	I	D	N	N	H	N	E	T	G
H	Y	O	N	R	V	O	R	N	E	A	N	Y	L	A	R
C	T	T	L	D	U	L	R	P	D	L	E	M	K	S	M
H	T	E	S	R	C	E	R	C	E	N	A	M	U	O	N
A	A	N	G	A	M	U	N	L	U	S	C	A	R	A	O
O	B	O	R	S	B	T	A	N	E	A	R	S	T	O	I
N	Y	G	U	L	I	I	V	E	R	D	S	U	Z	L	N
O	I	A	B	T	D	L	E	H	F	O	L	B	N	O	D
Y	O	M	E	D	A	R	T	H	V	V	A	D	E	R	U
R	R	R	R	B	U	B	M	E	F	D	E	A	N	L	C

BANE
BLOFELD
COLONEL KURTZ
DARTH VADER
DR EVIL
GRENDEL
HANS GRUBER

IAGO
KEVIN
KHAN
MAGNETO
MEDEA
MR DARK
NOAH CROSS

NORMAN BATES
NURSE RATCHED
ROY BATTY
SATAN
SAURON
SCAR

TWISTED tip: Characters with two names will have one of the names written without an extra letter.

57. CROSS WORDS

What's the TWIST?

Find each of the listed words and phrases in the grid.

Each entry in the grid is cross-shaped – either **X** or **+**. The letter at the centre of each cross-shape (S in this case) is used twice. All entries in the grid read horizontally from left to right for the first half of the word or phrase, then from top to bottom for the second half.

TWISTED tip: There are lots of double S-words in the entries, so if you look for SS in the grid there is a good chance it will be part of one of the listed words.

S	S	A	N	A	E	U	E	Y	R	O	T	S	E	I	O
S	S	D	E	I	I	S	N	T	C	D	U	I	C	P	S
U	D	I	S	H	O	I	S	S	D	U	C	S	S	S	Y
S	D	S	T	I	R	I	I	E	E	O	U	E	L	M	S
S	I	I	Y	U	M	D	I	B	S	L	D	S	O	Y	S
Y	B	S	S	S	U	E	I	S	O	D	I	S	T	R	D
S	S	B	C	T	I	R	A	C	T	S	T	E	S	S	S
D	A	E	I	E	S	S	S	L	C	L	S	D	S	T	S
I	E	A	N	S	S	I	T	E	I	S	O	S	E	S	R
D	I	S	P	L	D	S	M	Y	S	T	I	U	S	I	M
L	S	E	S	S	I	M	L	D	M	I	N	O	S	I	N
M	H	D	A	L	C	S	I	Y	S	T	T	E	E	L	A
S	T	I	N	O	S	M	D	S	S	S	D	I	S	S	Y
S	C	A	S	P	I	E	E	S	T	U	B	U	S	I	N
S	I	A	E	T	I	P	S	A	S	S	S	I	E	F	O
R	M	A	A	S	S	A	T	S	M	S	D	P	S	S	Y

ABSURDISTS
ASSESS
ASSIST
BUSINESSES
CASPIAN SEA
DESIROUSLY
DESPOTISMS
DISCOUNSEL
DISCOURSES
DISHONESTY
DISPLEASED
DISSATISFY
DISTRESSED
LISTLESSLY
LUSCIOUSLY
MASOCHISTS
MISTRESSES
MYSTICISMS
NOSINESSES
PESSIMISTS

58. WRAPAROUND

What's the TWIST?

Find each of the listed **cricket** themed words and phrases in the grid. They may be written forwards or backwards in any direction, including diagonally.

Entries can wrap around from one edge of the grid to the other, so imagine that the grid repeats immediately on all sides. Words and phrases that wrap around continue on the opposite side to correspond with where they would be on the repeated grid.

H T M U L M R F D N A O R E D A
S I L E T O T I E E U U K G L B
D S R S Y R A A P T B C F L B U
C A T D N N A Y Y M E S R B Y O
U A O L M E E L N A U V U G N K
R N R Y N A G E A B M R I F L Q
M E D K L R N R S T M Q E R S E
B O C A U G H T T B R E I F D B
N Q N N R F O W P A T E R L A Q
B R R L U Y L O U O D M E C F S
T C E L M O B I G T W I C K E T
M B L K A A B S C S F L A A A N
T T O L N H I O I F O N M A R A
O U N W D L I D N R N U L Y U M
H O R T L E G Y E N E M S T O S
B N L Y F E E K R N Y T S Y S T

TWISTED tip: Search for letters that appear infrequently in the word list; they will also be relatively infrequent in the grid.

BATSMAN
BOUNCER
BOUNDARY
CAUGHT
CENTURY
DRIVE
FAST BOWLER

FIELDER
FULL TOSS
GOOGLY
MAIDEN
NO-BALL
SEAM
SHORT LEG

SILLY MID-ON
SQUARE LEG
THIRD MAN
UMPIRE
WICKET
YORKER

59. OFF GRID

What's the TWIST?

Find each of the listed **chess grandmasters** in the grid.

The grid has a chequerboard design in which only every other square includes a letter.

R		R		S		D		Z		N		O		K	
	T		E		E		L		T		A		K		Y
M		A		K		L		O		I		M		E	
	O		R		S		I		N		N		M		L
K		R		R		A		M		R		I		I	
	R		P		A		L		E		A		E		T
Y		A		H		S		H		O		A		T	
	L		M		Y		C		O		L		S		S
C		D		N		S		H		E		T		V	
	A		A		I		A		K		A		O		S
K		R		F		K		H		U		L		P	
	A		L		L		I		N		A		A		D
E		R		S		N		T		P		S		N	
	U		P		E		O		O		S		A		T
O		W		O		N		T		K		N		A	
	P		E		V		I		Y		A		L		E

ADLY
ALEKHINE
ANAND
ARNOLD
CARLSEN
EUWE
FISCHER
KARPOV
KRAMNIK
LASKER
LEKO
MILES
MORPHY
SPASSKY
STAUNTON
STEINITZ
TAL
TARRASCH
TIMMAN
TOPALOV

TWISTED tip: Due to the shape of the grid, all the entries are found in diagonal directions.

60. SECRET WORDS

What's the TWIST?

Find each of the listed words in the grid. They may be written forwards or backwards in any direction, including diagonally.

Each entry in the word list contains at least one concealed **animal**; for example KARATE contains a hidden RAT. Delete the hidden animals from the words when searching for them in the grid. So for KARATE search for KAE.

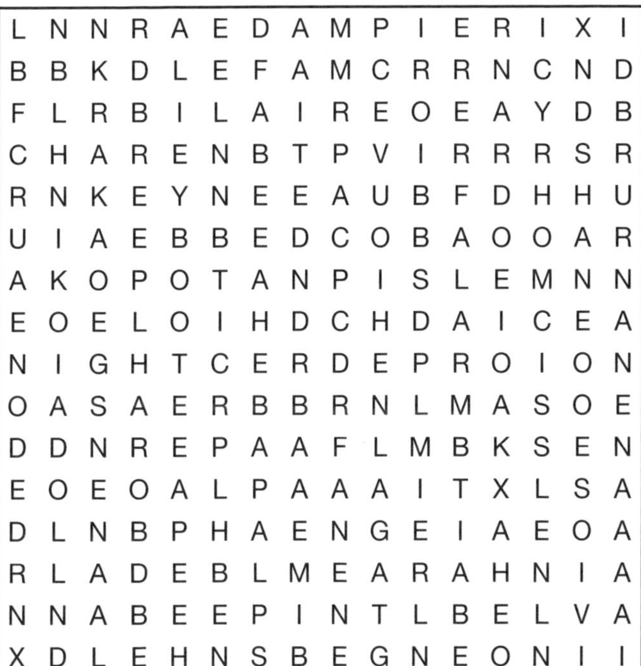

L	N	N	R	A	E	D	A	M	P	I	E	R	I	X	I
B	B	K	D	L	E	F	A	M	C	R	R	N	C	N	D
F	L	R	B	I	L	A	I	R	E	O	E	A	Y	D	B
C	H	A	R	E	N	B	T	P	V	I	R	R	R	S	R
R	N	K	E	Y	N	E	E	A	U	B	F	D	H	H	U
U	I	A	E	B	B	E	D	C	O	B	A	O	O	A	R
A	K	O	P	O	T	A	N	P	I	S	L	E	M	N	N
E	O	E	L	O	I	H	D	C	H	D	A	I	C	E	A
N	I	G	H	T	C	E	R	D	E	P	R	O	I	O	N
O	A	S	A	E	R	B	B	R	N	L	M	A	S	O	E
D	D	N	R	E	P	A	A	F	L	M	B	K	S	E	N
E	O	E	O	A	L	P	A	A	A	I	T	X	L	S	A
D	L	N	B	P	H	A	E	N	G	E	I	A	E	O	A
R	L	A	D	E	B	L	M	E	A	R	A	H	N	I	A
N	N	A	B	E	E	P	I	N	T	L	B	E	L	V	A
X	D	L	E	H	N	S	B	E	G	N	E	O	N	I	I

TWISTED tip: Entries in the grid always contain at least three letters.

BENEVOLENCE
BILLIONAIRE
BREWERY
COMMANDEER
COWARDICE
DASHBOARD
DISOWNED
EPIGRAPH
EXPANDABLE
FALSE ALARM
GLOBE-TROTTER
HOTELKEEPER
KARATE
MAHOGANY
NIGHTMARE
PROBATION
PUBLICATION
SHAREHOLDER
UNBEARABLE
VAMOOSED

61. WRAPAROUND

What's the TWIST?

Find each of the listed **Bond villains** in the grid. They may be written forwards or backwards in any direction, including diagonally.

Entries can wrap around from one edge of the grid to the other, so imagine that the grid repeats immediately on all sides. Names that wrap around continue on the opposite side to correspond with where they would be on the repeated grid.

V	D	A	L	H	N	O	O	O	E	M	R	N	D	E	A
R	Z	L	K	O	T	I	N	L	L	K	S	B	R	D	T
I	E	N	E	L	V	L	M	S	N	D	N	F	H	F	S
S	H	M	B	F	E	M	A	O	U	N	F	A	O	A	U
T	A	W	I	S	O	B	T	T	D	I	V	I	M	L	G
M	S	R	R	L	C	L	B	O	H	L	L	R	N	L	K
R	O	S	D	M	I	M	B	C	I	H	A	U	A	G	R
C	T	R	L	M	R	O	E	S	U	G	B	R	J	C	E
R	A	K	I	N	G	L	L	G	G	A	E	L	E	K	T
N	T	I	N	I	R	U	O	A	R	V	R	N	O	N	S
Z	S	G	Z	I	O	D	R	S	R	G	S	D	E	R	E
E	I	S	C	A	R	A	M	A	N	G	A	I	R	R	V
B	R	L	R	A	I	O	C	E	M	N	O	O	E	C	A
L	K	G	X	S	L	T	Z	E	E	C	T	A	O	T	R
O	O	R	C	L	O	O	H	X	G	F	A	E	S	M	G
R	S	R	I	I	A	V	G	M	A	D	N	E	O	R	V

TWISTED tip: The words in this puzzle have lots of letters, so many of them wrap around the edges of the grid.

BLOFELD
DOMINIC GREENE
ELEKTRA KING
ELLIOT CARVER
EMILIO LARGO
GENERAL ORLOV
GOLDFINGER
GUSTAV GRAVES
HUGO DRAX
JULIUS NO
KRISTATOS
LE CHIFFRE
MAX ZORIN
MILTON KREST
MR BIG
MR WHITE
RAOUL SILVA
RENARD
ROSA KLEBB
SCARAMANGA

62. LITTLE CLUES

What's the TWIST?

The names of 20 **items of clothing** are hidden in the grid. They may be written forwards or backwards in any direction, including diagonally.

Work out what the words are with the help of the initial letters given. The initials are listed alphabetically, which should help when there is more than one entry starting with the same letter.

```
S K I R T N K T S Y A W E D R A
S A C S W Y R R R J S U I S S S
T S O A S I D N E T J O O E S L
S A R I H E U W S N R S T N E I
T C O S R R R H U N T T A G S G
O G T C R E O D O S H E G S A N
C S D K T O T T R O J I Y H M H
K T A I D S W A T D N N N O A T
I E Y I C T I T E G I T S R J E
N R E E U N J A S W P S P T Y E
G R E S S A O B W R S N T S P S
S U N D E R P A N T S E M S E U
F G R H I A E E C E E L F I N O
G T I E S E E J N K A O L C A L
S N A G I D R A C A A C L E M B
R B K A A G N O R A S A A S G S
```

B...
C...
C...
D...
F...
H...
J...
J...
L...
P...
S...
S...
S...
S...
S...
S...
T...
T...
U...
W...

TWISTED tip: One of the two J entries is JERSEY and one of the S entries is SARI.

63. VOWELLESS

What's the TWIST?

Find each of the listed words and phrases in the grid. They may be written forwards or backwards in any direction, including diagonally.

Ignore all vowels in the words and phrases when searching in the grid. So for AUBERGINE search for BRGN.

H Q Q M R L L R C T S P L C M T
T M H L L S C M R N C G T R N C
Q H N N F G N R S N R Q R R M R
G L R N T S R N Q R V L R G S T
G R S L M C G D G L R L L N C N
T H V L N S R L T L G L F T C N
R D M G P H S N S S C N S M D L
T T R F L C S G S T M N L T N R
S B R C G R M M D T M C C L L S
C H Q M P L D L T M N V G M T S
L R L H R G N Q C R M P L R R L
C R T T L T V T R C R C C C N R
C T N T D N L R M S S G N S Q L
T S R P L R S N L S N T L L C N
N C R C S N C N R P R Q S T N N
T R C Q G R R R G V N C N V G G

AUBERGINE
AUTHORIAL
COLLEAGUE
COURTEOUS
DAIQUIRIS
EGREGIOUS
ELOCUTION
EMOTIONAL
EVACUATED
GUINEA PIG
HOUSEMATE
INSINUATE
LIQUORICE
MALICIOUS
PIECEMEAL
QUALIFIES
RELIGIOUS
REPUDIATE
UNANIMOUS
VARIATION

TWISTED tip: Only one letter in this grid is used by more than one entry.

64. THIS AND THAT

What's the TWIST?

Find each of the listed missing words in the grid. They may be written forwards or backwards in any direction, including diagonally.

First complete each entry in the word list to make a well-known phrase. For example, THICK AND .... completes as THICK AND THIN, so you must then search for THIN in the grid.

```
D N O N I N L N N C E A A R R W
O E B E E E R I A S E M D R A C
E A M E T D I E B I A E O T E E
E A E A R A M D A D L T E N E T
T L T E N N K O R A E R T S S D
S H R I S D R E E A F R P S B T
M R I E E E D S H D E I W L S E
C T M N R R N E E K H S O S O E
A A E S S E R P H C K O O S O M
G E S I W H R T F C D B S U I W
S D L K A A O O O E U R F E R S
R N M W E E R S D T E E D B H E
B S E E T G T E T P S I L S E E
M D D D E L L E P D L A S C A T
D F I T T U R E R S O E L L T E
R K W C I E P Y E H L L L N E B
```

BREAD AND ....
FIRST AND ....
FISH AND ....
FLESH AND ....
FORGIVE AND ....
FRONT AND ....
FUN AND ....
GIVE AND ....
HAMMER AND ....
HEMMED AND ....
HIGH AND ....
SALT AND ....
SHIRT AND ....
SHOES AND ....
SIGNED AND ....
SLIP AND ....
SOAP AND ....
SUPPLY AND ....
SWEET AND ....
THICK AND ....

TWISTED tip: Three of the missing words are CENTRE, SLIDE and LAST.

65. LEFTOVER LETTERS

What's the TWIST?

Find each of the listed **pop song titles** in the grid. They may be written forwards or backwards in any direction, including diagonally.

Each entry in the grid includes one extra letter (not shown in the word list). Make a note of the extra letter beside the corresponding song title in the list. Then use the letters to spell out a related phrase in the space at the bottom of the page.

AT LAST
BILLIE JEAN
CALL ME
COMMON PEOPLE
DREAM ON
HALLELUJAH
HEY JUDE
HURT
I'M A BELIEVER
IMAGINE
IRIS
I WANT YOU BACK
LE FREAK
MACARENA
MY GIRL
NIGHT FEVER
RESPECT
SOMEBODY TO LOVE
THE TWIST
THRILLER

TWISTED tip: The hidden phrase refers to an old-fashioned way of listening to music.

66. CROSS WORDS

What's the TWIST?

Find each of the listed words and phrases in the grid.

Each entry in the grid is cross-shaped – either **X** or **+**. The letter at the centre of each cross-shape (L in this case) is used twice. All entries in the grid read horizontally from left to right for the first half of the word or phrase, then from top to bottom for the second half.

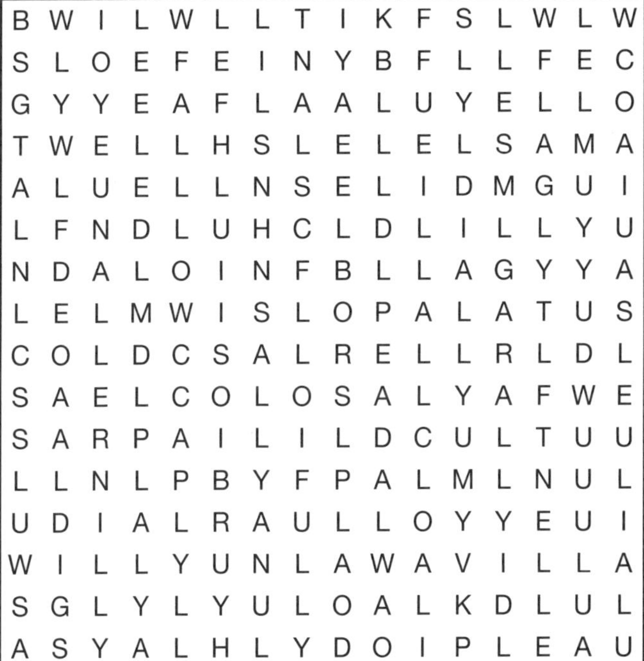

B	W	I	L	W	L	L	T	I	K	F	S	L	W	L	W
S	L	O	E	F	E	I	N	Y	B	F	L	L	F	E	C
G	Y	Y	E	A	F	L	A	A	L	U	Y	E	L	L	O
T	W	E	L	L	H	S	L	E	L	E	L	S	A	M	A
A	L	U	E	L	L	N	S	E	L	I	D	M	G	U	I
L	F	N	D	L	U	H	C	L	D	L	I	L	L	Y	U
N	D	A	L	O	I	N	F	B	L	L	A	G	Y	Y	A
L	E	L	M	W	I	S	L	O	P	A	L	A	T	U	S
C	O	L	D	C	S	A	L	R	E	L	L	R	L	D	L
S	A	E	L	C	O	L	O	S	A	L	Y	A	F	W	E
S	A	R	P	A	I	L	I	L	D	C	U	L	T	U	U
L	L	N	L	P	B	Y	F	P	A	L	M	L	N	U	L
U	D	I	A	L	R	A	U	L	L	O	Y	Y	E	U	I
W	I	L	L	Y	U	N	L	A	W	A	V	I	L	L	A
S	G	L	Y	L	Y	U	L	O	A	L	K	D	L	U	L
A	S	Y	A	L	H	L	Y	D	O	I	P	L	E	A	U

ALKALI
COLD-CALLER
COLOSSALLY
CULTURALLY
FLAILS
GLADLY
GLIBLY
GLUMLY
HULLABALOO
PALATIALLY
PILLOWSLIP
SALMONELLA
SELF-STYLED
SLOWLY
UNLABELLED
UNLAWFULLY
VILLANELLE
WELL HEELED
WILLY-NILLY
YELLOW FLAG

TWISTED tip: Look for an infrequently used letter, such as F, to start making headway with this puzzle.

67. WRAPAROUND

What's the TWIST?

Find each of the listed **weather** themed words and phrases in the grid. They may be written forwards or backwards in any direction, including diagonally.

Entries can wrap around from one edge of the grid to the other, so imagine that the grid repeats immediately on all sides. Words and phrases that wrap around continue on the opposite side to correspond with where they would be on the repeated grid.

TWISTED tip: The shortest word in this puzzle does not wrap around the edge of the grid.

```
L M E G P H L O P C I B D N T O
E E O T N C L W W Y E O L E N S
B T L R N G E E C O T E N N N A
R R I O O U B R H S O D H T O N
D H E N S N H O E O U U W H C T
G N I E Z A N P N C U Z O G E A
A E N I Z O M S S L D H W N P G
K I C E R E E G L T N M B L A C
H L Y S T H U N D E R T S S I S
A S C A Q W H G H O E T T R K G
H E L E E U R H T C R T R R C A
R T O O R W A S L E W U G E R L
O W N D N I W L R I H W R E S E
W U E I L O T F L I E I B O D R
N W D Y N O O S N O M C E H N O
I G R S S G R H L E R E A A R S
```

BLACK ICE
BREEZE
CLOUDS
CYCLONE
FOG
GALE
HAIL
HAZE
HURRICANE
LIGHTNING
MONSOON
SHOWER
SLEET
SNOWSTORM
SQUALL
TEMPEST
THUNDER
TORNADO
TYPHOON
WHIRLWIND

68. SHAPED WORDS

What's the TWIST?

Find each of the listed C-words in the grid.

Each entry in the grid is found in the shape of a letter C. Entries may be read in either direction along the body of the C and the C-shapes are never rotated. One entry is marked as an example.

O C A C C I A C I C S M M H C L
V H M R C R O C V L R H C N L C
E R E L C A E T I L R C R C A C
L C Y C N C V N E L E P A A U M
R L R C I C H N N C A M S H S E
H O P S C A S A H C S V S C C M
C C C A H O C S A A S S O E R C
I L C U M U L M P L N H S T S S
M O L I T O E A L T U C C S L K
O A K C R E C L C A S C C U L O
L C H L P E U E R C K I C L C A
S N A A C C Q C I O C N L P P I
R C U N A U N O C O H C H C Y P
E S L C L A E A M K S M O S E A
S S U E E I L C C C E R R D C T
H C E S C O U U E A M E R S I V

TWISTED tip: The middle part of the C-shape is always at least three letters long, and corresponds with the centre of the word, so may be easiest to find first.

CALCIUM
CAMEL
CAUSE
CHANNEL
CHORD
CINCH
CIVIL
CLAMP
CLOAK
CLUES
CLUSTER
~~COACH~~
CONQUER
COOKS
COVER
CRASH
CREAM
CRESS
CUTLASS
CYCLOPS

69. SECRET WORDS

What's the TWIST?

Find each of the listed words and phrases in the grid. They may be written forwards or backwards in any direction, including diagonally.

Each entry in the word list conceals the word MIND. Delete MIND from the words and phrases when searching for them in the grid. So for OPEN-MINDED search for OPENED.

TWISTED tip: You only need to eliminate MIND from each clue, making this puzzle relatively straightforward.

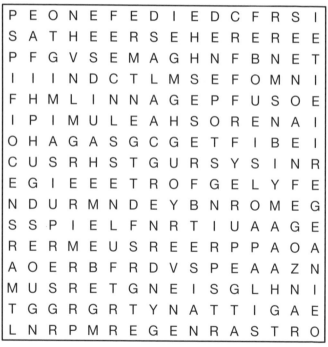

P	E	O	N	E	F	E	D	I	E	D	C	F	R	S	I
S	A	T	H	E	E	R	S	E	H	E	R	E	R	E	E
P	F	G	V	S	E	M	A	G	H	N	F	B	N	E	T
I	I	I	N	D	C	T	L	M	S	E	F	O	M	N	I
F	H	M	L	I	N	N	A	G	E	P	F	U	S	O	E
I	P	I	M	U	L	E	A	H	S	O	R	E	N	A	I
O	H	A	G	A	S	G	C	G	E	T	F	I	B	E	I
C	U	S	R	H	S	T	G	U	R	S	Y	S	I	N	R
E	G	I	E	E	E	T	R	O	F	G	E	L	Y	F	E
N	D	U	R	M	N	D	E	Y	B	N	R	O	M	E	G
S	S	P	I	E	L	F	N	R	T	I	U	A	A	G	E
R	E	R	M	E	U	S	R	E	E	R	P	P	A	O	A
A	O	E	R	B	F	R	D	V	S	P	E	A	A	Z	N
M	U	S	R	E	T	G	N	E	I	S	G	L	H	N	I
T	G	G	R	G	R	T	Y	N	A	T	T	I	G	A	E
L	N	R	P	M	R	E	G	E	N	R	A	S	T	R	O

ABSENT-MINDED
CHEMIN DE FER
CHILDMINDER
FILM INDUSTRY
FRAME OF MIND
HIGH-MINDEDNESS
HIVE MIND
IN YOUR MIND'S EYE
MASTERMIND
MIND GAMES
MIND MAPPING
MIND-BOGGLING
MINDFULNESS
NEVER YOU MIND
OF ONE MIND
OPEN-MINDED
REMINDERS
SPRINGS TO MIND
VITAMIN D
ZAMINDAR

70. WARPED VISION

What's the TWIST?

Find each of the listed **types of creepy-crawly** in the grid. They may be written forwards or backwards in any direction, including diagonally.

The rows and columns that make up the grid have been twisted, but you should still solve the puzzle as if they were perfectly straight.

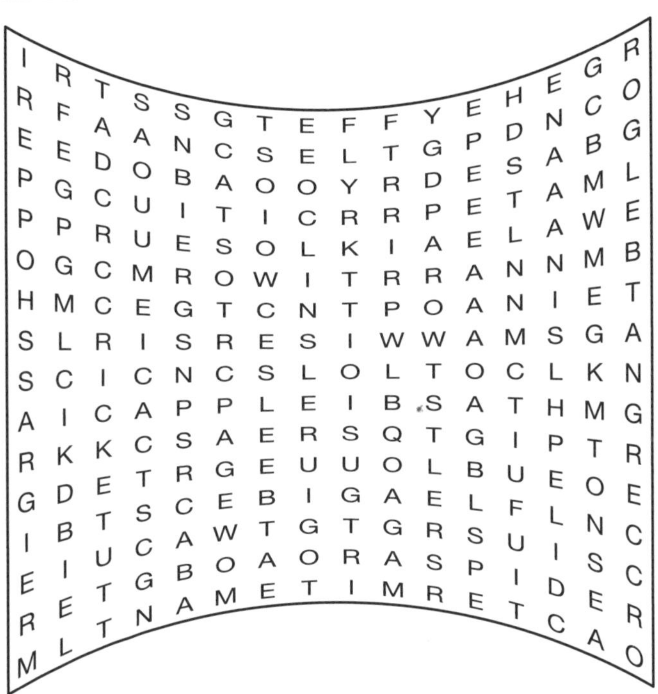

ANT
BEE
BUG
CATERPILLAR
CENTIPEDE
COCKROACH
CRICKET
FLEA
FLY
GNAT
GRASSHOPPER
GRUB
MAGGOT
MOSQUITO
SLUG
SNAIL
SPIDER
TERMITE
WASP
WORM

TWISTED tip: Look for the longest entries first and the shortest ones last.

What's the TWIST?

The names of 20 **fruits** are hidden in the grid. They may be written forwards or backwards in any direction, including diagonally.

Work out what the fruits are with the help of the initial letters given. The initials are listed alphabetically, which should help when there is more than one entry starting with the same letter.

Y	C	H	E	R	R	Y	N	G	Y	E	E	Y	R	L	L
R	E	O	O	R	A	O	R	R	O	T	Y	I	S	H	Y
R	A	G	A	U	L	R	R	A	R	A	A	T	N	R	T
E	N	Y	W	E	E	E	E	R	L	N	R	L	L	G	A
B	E	W	M	A	B	E	N	E	K	A	E	A	R	C	R
R	C	C	E	P	H	A	S	O	W	R	L	A	E	A	E
E	T	R	S	C	E	T	M	B	N	G	P	E	Y	B	E
D	A	A	Y	M	H	Y	E	P	I	E	P	R	R	N	K
L	R	L	O	A	A	R	B	H	H	M	A	G	R	O	A
E	I	A	E	A	R	N	H	R	E	O	Y	N	E	M	L
A	N	Y	G	Y	O	C	A	P	I	P	M	P	B	E	I
E	E	E	G	E	A	R	P	N	E	W	S	M	K	L	M
L	A	M	E	E	R	E	A	L	A	A	I	E	C	Y	E
R	H	L	P	C	E	W	A	N	M	B	R	K	A	A	G
N	A	M	A	N	G	O	A	R	G	E	O	P	L	K	W
E	S	A	T	S	U	M	A	A	E	E	T	A	B	P	S

A..
B..
B..
C..
E..
G..
K..
L..
L..
L..
M..
M..
N..
O..
P..
P..
P..
R..
S..
S..

TWISTED tip: Four of the fruits have names that end in -BERRY.

72. SHAPED WORDS

What's the TWIST?

Find each of the listed n-words in the grid.

Each entry in the grid is found in the shape of a lower-case n. Entries may be read in either direction along the body of the n and the n-shapes are never rotated. One entry is marked as an example.

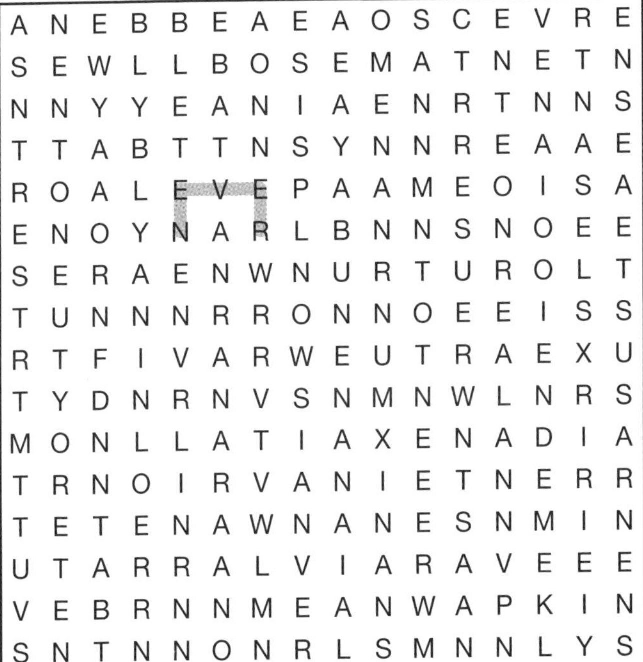

A	N	E	B	B	E	A	E	A	O	S	C	E	V	R	E
S	E	W	L	L	B	O	S	E	M	A	T	N	E	T	N
N	N	Y	Y	E	A	N	I	A	E	N	R	T	N	N	S
T	T	A	B	T	T	N	S	Y	N	N	R	E	A	A	E
R	O	A	L	E	V	E	P	A	A	M	E	O	I	S	A
E	N	O	Y	N	A	R	L	B	N	N	S	N	O	E	E
S	E	R	A	E	N	W	N	U	R	T	U	R	O	L	T
T	U	N	N	N	R	R	O	N	N	O	E	E	I	S	S
R	T	F	I	V	A	R	W	E	U	T	R	A	E	X	U
T	Y	D	N	R	N	V	S	N	M	N	W	L	N	R	S
M	O	N	L	L	A	T	I	A	X	E	N	A	D	I	A
T	R	N	O	I	R	V	A	N	I	E	T	N	E	R	R
T	E	T	E	N	A	W	N	A	N	E	S	N	M	I	N
U	T	A	R	R	A	L	V	I	A	R	A	V	E	E	E
V	E	B	R	N	N	M	E	A	N	W	A	P	K	I	N
S	N	T	N	N	O	N	R	L	S	M	N	N	L	Y	S

NADIR
NAIVE
NAMES
NAPKINS
NARRATE
NARROWS
NASCENT

NEAREST
NEMESIS
NERVE
NEUTRAL
~~NEVER~~
NEWLY
NEXUS

NIFTY
NIRVANA
NOBLE
NOISE
NOTABLY
NURTURE

TWISTED tip: The middle of the n-shape is always three letters wide.

73. CROSS WORDS

What's the TWIST?

Find each of the listed words in the grid.

Each entry in the grid is cross-shaped – either **X** or **+**. The letter at the centre of each cross-shape (A in this case) is used twice. All entries in the grid read horizontally from left to right for the first half of the word then from top to bottom for the second half.

TWISTED tip: Try to predict how some of the entries in this grid might overlap.

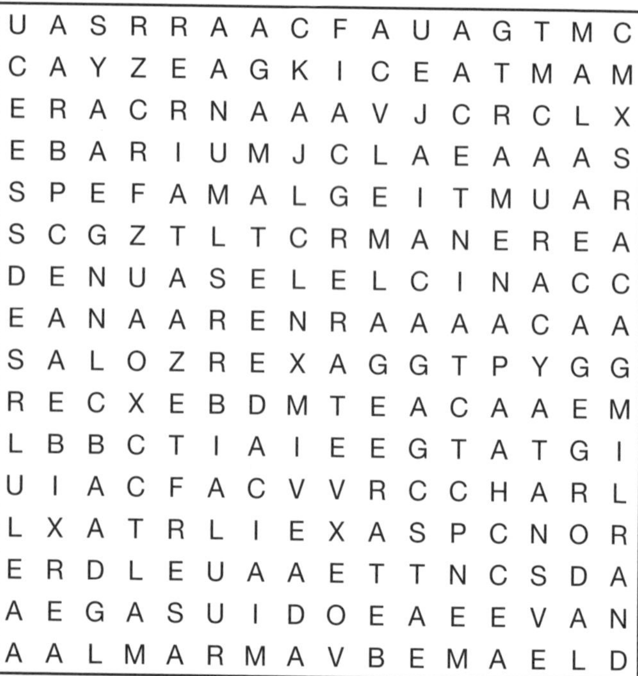

U	A	S	R	R	A	A	C	F	A	U	A	G	T	M	C
C	A	Y	Z	E	A	G	K	I	C	E	A	T	M	A	M
E	R	A	C	R	N	A	A	A	V	J	C	R	C	L	X
E	B	A	R	I	U	M	J	C	L	A	E	A	A	A	S
S	P	E	F	A	M	A	L	G	E	I	T	M	U	A	R
S	C	G	Z	T	L	T	C	R	M	A	N	E	R	E	A
D	E	N	U	A	S	E	L	E	L	C	I	N	A	C	C
E	A	N	A	A	R	E	N	R	A	A	A	A	C	A	A
S	A	L	O	Z	R	E	X	A	G	G	T	P	Y	G	G
R	E	C	X	E	B	D	M	T	E	A	C	A	A	E	M
L	B	B	C	T	I	A	I	E	E	G	T	A	T	G	I
U	I	A	C	F	A	C	V	V	R	C	C	H	A	R	L
L	X	A	T	R	L	I	E	X	A	S	P	C	N	O	R
E	R	D	L	E	U	A	A	E	T	T	N	C	S	D	A
A	E	G	A	S	U	I	D	O	E	A	E	E	V	A	N
A	A	L	M	A	R	M	A	V	B	E	M	A	E	L	D

AMALGAMATE
BANTAM
BAZAAR
CHARLATANS
COASTGUARD
DEACTIVATE
EXACERBATE
EXAGGERATE
EXASPERATE
FACIAL
INACCURACY
JACKAL
JAGUAR
MAMMAL
MANIAC
RACIAL
REACTIVATE
SANDAL
SPACECRAFT
VANDAL

74. SYMBOLIC

What's the TWIST?

Find each of the listed words and phrases in the grid. They may be written forwards or backwards in any direction, including diagonally.

All occurrences of DASH and DOT in the listed words and phrases have been replaced by - or . respectively in the grid. So for BALDERDASH search for BALDER-.

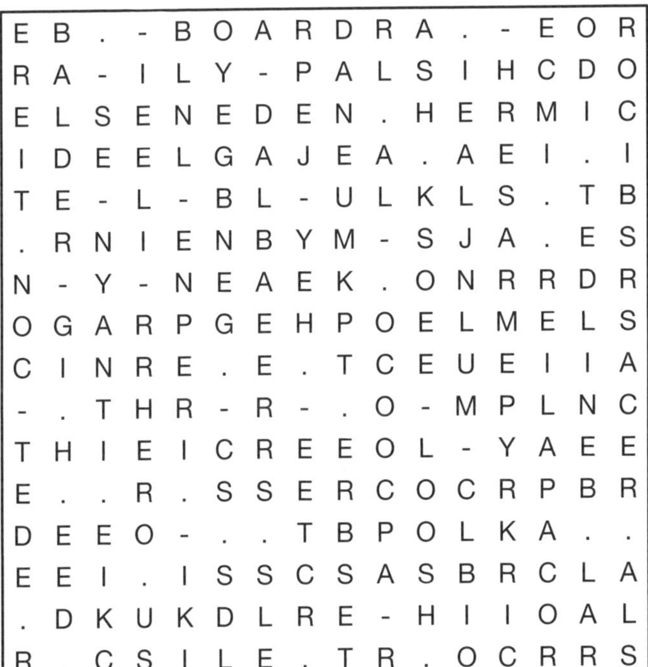

E B . - B O A R D R A . - E O R
R A - I L Y - P A L S I H C D O
E L S E N E D E N . H E R M I C
I D E E L G A J E A . A E I . I
T E - L - B L - U L K L S . T B
. R N I E N B Y M - S J A . E S
N - Y - N E A E K . O N R R D R
O G A R P G E H P O E L M E L S
C I N R E . E . T C E U E I I A
- . T H R - R - . O - M P L N C
T H I E I C R E E O L - Y A E E
E . . R . S S E R C O C R P B R
D E E O - . . T B P O L K A . .
E E I . I S S C S A S B R C L A
. D K U K D L R E - H I I O A L
R . C S I L E . T R . O C R R S

TWISTED tip: Each entry contains only one DOT or DASH.

ANECDOTE
ANTIDOTE
BALDERDASH
BERMUDA SHORTS
CONDOTTIERE
DASHBOARD
DASHIKI
DASHING
DOTINGLY
DOTTED LINE
ENDOTHERMIC
HABERDASHERY
HERODOTUS
JUDAS HOLE
PEBBLE-DASH
PERIDOT
POLKADOT
SACERDOTAL
SACKCLOTH AND ASHES
SLAPDASH

75. EMPTY INSIDE

What's the TWIST?

Find each of the listed **camping** themed words and phrases in the grid. They may be written forwards or backwards in any direction, including diagonally.

Fill in the 36 blank squares in the centre of the grid as you place the entries.

O	I	N	O	A	D	S	R	S	P	T	D	T	N	R	T
R	T	L	E	C	G	R	T	E	E	H	N	O	H	G	R
S	O	H	T	G	N	A	B	S	L	R	O	C	R	N	H
A	I	P	N	A	F	G	S	T	B	I	R	I	C	Y	O
E	P	E	E	B	I	A	N	O	A	O	A	Q	T	P	A
A	I	N	M	G							E	R	M	O	S
O	S	E	O	N							T	G	T	N	A
K	L	S	S	I							B	S	R	A	E
E	E	B	Q	P							U	L	E	C	L
T	K	N	U	E							G	S	A	A	K
M	H	A	I	E							S	M	O	I	T
T	L	I	T	L	K	T	T	I	P	C	P	C	I	T	A
C	E	K	O	S	I	E	O	H	S	S	R	C	A	P	E
T	C	F	N	O	T	R	P	G	I	A	A	S	T	S	S
O	O	A	E	T	S	A	C	T	H	G	Y	A	H	N	D
L	A	N	T	E	R	N	E	C	E	P	P	M	A	B	P

BUG SPRAY
CAMPSITE
CANOPY
CHARCOAL
FIRST AID KIT
FOLDING CHAIR
GAS CANISTER
GAS COOKER
HIKING BOOTS
LANTERN
MOSQUITO NET
PEGS
PICNIC TABLE
POTS AND PANS
ROPE
SLEEPING BAG
STAKE
THERMOS
TORCH
TRAILER

TWISTED tip: This puzzle contains lots of entries that run in the same direction.

76. LEFTOVER LETTERS

What's the TWIST?

Find each of the listed **time** themed words in the grid. They may be written forwards or backwards in any direction, including diagonally.

Each entry in the grid includes one extra letter (not shown in the word list). Make a note of the extra letter beside the corresponding word in the list. Then use the letters to spell out a related phrase in the space at the bottom of the page.

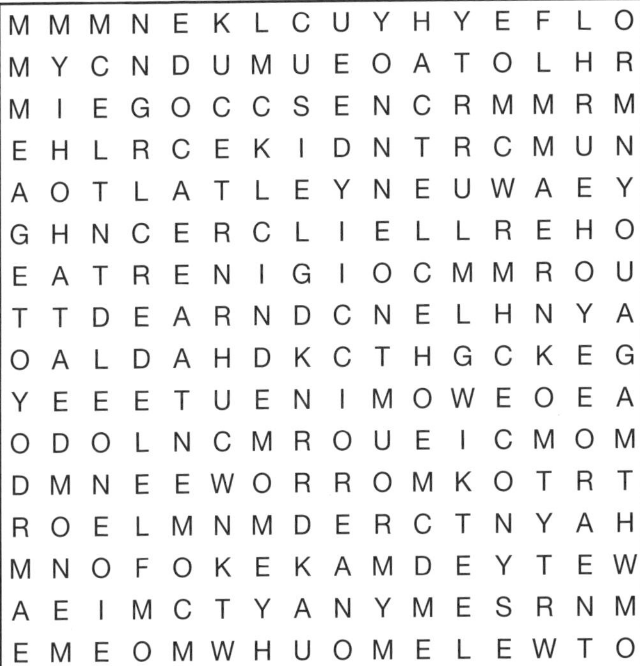

M	M	M	N	E	K	L	C	U	Y	H	Y	E	F	L	O
M	Y	C	N	D	U	M	U	E	O	A	T	O	L	H	R
M	I	E	G	O	C	C	S	E	N	C	R	M	M	R	M
E	H	L	R	C	E	K	I	D	N	T	R	C	M	U	N
A	O	T	L	A	T	L	E	Y	N	E	U	W	A	E	Y
G	H	N	C	E	R	C	L	I	E	L	L	R	E	H	O
E	A	T	R	E	N	I	G	I	O	C	M	M	R	O	U
T	T	D	E	A	R	N	D	C	N	E	L	H	N	Y	A
O	A	L	D	A	H	D	K	C	T	H	G	C	K	E	G
Y	E	E	E	T	U	E	N	I	M	O	W	E	O	E	A
O	D	O	L	N	C	M	R	O	U	E	I	C	M	O	M
D	M	N	E	E	W	O	R	R	O	M	K	O	T	R	T
R	O	E	L	M	N	M	D	E	R	C	T	N	Y	A	H
M	N	O	F	O	K	E	K	A	M	D	E	Y	T	E	W
A	E	I	M	C	T	Y	A	N	Y	M	E	S	R	N	M
E	M	E	O	M	W	H	U	O	M	E	L	E	W	T	O

CENTURY
CLOCK
DAY
DECADE
EARLY
FORTNIGHT
HOUR
LATE
METRONOME
MILLENNIUM
MINUTE
MOMENT
MONTH
SECOND
TODAY
TOMORROW
WATCH
WEEK
YEAR
YESTERDAY

TWISTED tip: M is the most common starting letter; search for Ms to help you find entries quickly.

....

77. WARPED VISION

What's the TWIST?

Find each of the listed **plumbing** themed words and phrases in the grid. They may be written forwards or backwards in any direction, including diagonally.

The rows and columns that make up the grid have been twisted, but you should still solve the puzzle as if they were perfectly straight.

TWISTED tip: Try drawing feint lines through each horizontal, vertical and diagonal line to help you keep track of how the letters connect.

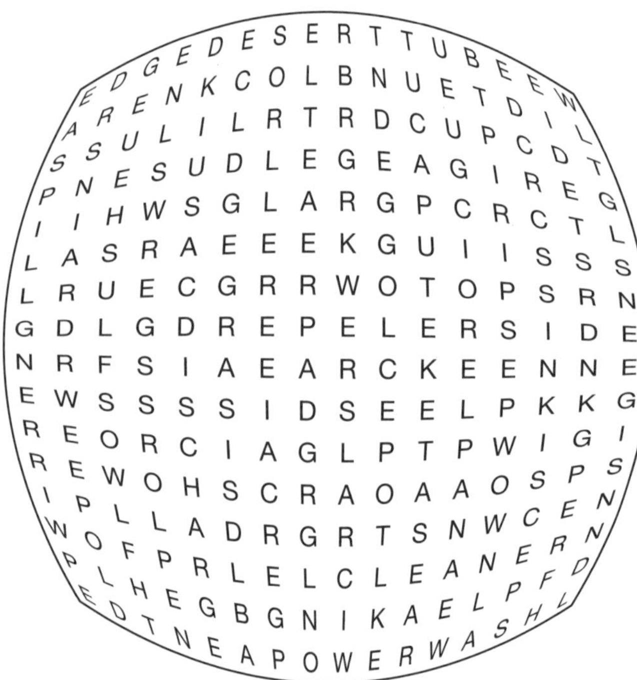

CLEANER
CLOGGED
DELUGE
DISCHARGE
DRAIN
FLUSH
LEAKING
PIPING
POWER WASH
SEEPAGE
SEWAGE
SHOWER
SINK
SOLDER
SPILL
TAP
TUBE
UNBLOCK
WATER PRESSURE
WELDING

78. SECRET WORDS

What's the TWIST?

Find each of the listed words in the grid. They may be written forwards or backwards in any direction, including diagonally.

Each entry in the word list contains three letter As, to make up a concealed AAA battery; for example RAMADAN. Delete the three hidden As from the words when searching for them in the grid. So for RAMADAN search for RMDN.

ADVANTAGE
BARBARIAN
CANADIAN
DISAPPEARANCE
EGALITARIAN
FAMILIARISATION
GRAMMATICALLY
HUMANITARIAN
INCAPACITATE
KAZAKHSTAN
LASAGNA
MANHATTAN
NIAGARA
ORGANISATIONAL
PARACETAMOL
RAMADAN
SALAMANDER
TOTALITARIAN
UNGRAMMATICAL
VALETUDINARIAN

TWISTED tip: Remember that you are only removing the As, and not any other vowels present in the listed words.

79. SHAPED WORDS

What's the TWIST?

Find each of the listed **zigzag** themed words in the grid.

Each entry in the grid is found in the shape of a zigzag, reading in any of the four diagonal directions. One entry is marked as an example.

E D E R I I S E D E C W D G D S
W E L K D E R N E I R R I N E G
L A E N I T U M K N T N D I I N
D E I E R W N E L D W I E L L D
E V E K U G A D N S N I V E E D
I A E N N E V I S S D W I S T W
U V W T I R E W U O T S W I T D
N W E N I G A Y V U N K T I S E
G R P G N E D S N E I S G E W D
S E E L Y I E V A K K A V R I C
M D G G S D I I A I N N I R N G
E R A D R E D D T I G G N R I V
S T I E D A A E D N G T D E E D
D E M P I C U R H S A A N O K S
Y R I T N E R V T N M E R O E D
W C R N E B N E D G D N C E O V

BENT
CRIMPED
CRINKLED
CROOKED
CURVED
DEVIATING
DIVERGING
~~MEANDERING~~
SERPENTINE
SINUOUS
SNAKING
STRAGGLY
SWERVING
SWIVELLING
THREADED
TURNED
TWISTED
WEAVED
WINDING
WRINKLED

TWISTED tip: Zigzags may read either across-down-across-down and so on, or down-across-down-across and so on.

80. CROSS WORDS

What's the TWIST?

Find each of the listed words in the grid.

Each entry in the grid is cross-shaped – either **X** or **+**. The letter at the centre of each cross-shape (I in this case) is used twice. All entries in the grid read horizontally from left to right for the first half of the word, then from top to bottom for the second half.

ALIENATION
AMIABILITY
BIGWIG
BIONIC
CHIEFTAINS
CHILBLAINS
CITRIC
EMISSARIES
EVIDENTIAL
FLICKERING
FRIENDLIER
LIMPID
LIQUID
MOISTURISE
PINKIE
SLIPPERIER
TIDBIT
VICTIM
VIOLIN
WITHIN

TWISTED tip: As the first half of the entries in the grid never read backwards, these word searches can actually be easier to solve than regular ones.

81. THIS AND THAT

What's the TWIST?

Find each of the listed missing words in the grid. They may be written forwards or backwards in any direction, including diagonally.

First complete each entry in the word list to make a well-known phrase. For example, WAR AND .... completes as WAR AND PEACE, so you must then search for PEACE in the grid.

E	F	B	L	I	E	E	E	E	T	C	E	L	L	T	I
G	K	L	E	E	N	N	O	T	U	I	N	C	K	O	W
R	N	E	J	D	C	R	P	N	P	A	N	L	U	I	L
G	W	I	E	K	N	E	A	U	W	D	P	S	H	F	U
K	L	B	K	L	A	N	F	O	R	U	N	N	E	E	R
L	S	G	N	C	L	F	U	T	N	O	R	R	R	N	E
P	P	W	E	F	I	W	N	I	I	E	B	R	E	R	D
E	Y	L	E	N	F	K	N	T	U	O	A	E	A	L	L
P	Y	L	G	D	T	F	A	W	T	O	N	N	A	W	C
L	I	E	S	I	C	L	W	H	E	K	L	U	G	E	N
E	O	T	E	Y	U	O	E	E	G	F	R	S	D	V	A
R	L	L	O	B	E	R	R	M	O	I	L	O	I	L	L
F	O	S	I	D	E	V	E	E	E	I	W	U	F	R	E
E	F	R	I	D	E	W	R	H	L	N	N	E	I	E	E
T	T	E	R	C	W	T	L	Y	C	B	I	L	T	V	R
T	G	O	G	E	N	D	E	K	L	E	K	W	H	D	N

ADAM AND ....
ALIVE AND ....
ANT AND ....
CHEESE AND ....
FRY AND ....
HOT AND ....
HUFFING AND ....
HUSBAND AND ....
IN AND ....
JACK AND ....
KNIFE AND ....
LADIES AND ....
LAW AND ....
SHIRT AND ....
SONNY AND ....
TATE AND ....
TRIAL AND ....
TRIALS AND ....
UP AND ....
WAR AND ....

TWISTED tip: Five of the missing words are names of people, one is a company and another is a book.

82. LEFTOVER LETTERS

What's the TWIST?

Find each of the listed **types of occupation** in the grid. They may be written forwards or backwards in any direction, including diagonally.

Each entry in the grid includes one extra letter (not shown in the word list). Make a note of the extra letter beside the corresponding occupation in the list. Then use the letters to spell out a related phrase in the space at the bottom of the page.

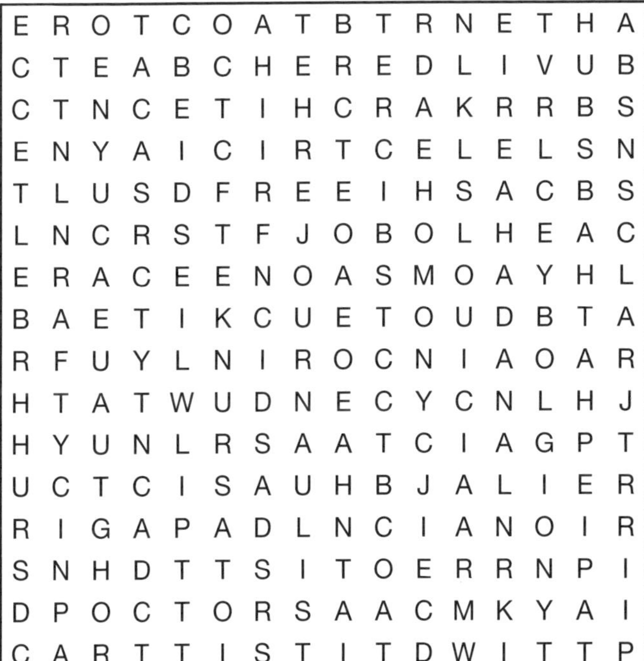

E	R	O	T	C	O	A	T	B	T	R	N	E	T	H	A
C	T	E	A	B	C	H	E	R	E	D	L	I	V	U	B
C	T	N	C	E	T	I	H	C	R	A	K	R	R	B	S
E	N	Y	A	I	C	I	R	T	C	E	L	E	L	S	N
T	L	U	S	D	F	R	E	E	I	H	S	A	C	B	S
L	N	C	R	S	T	F	J	O	B	O	L	H	E	A	C
E	R	A	C	E	E	N	O	A	S	M	O	A	Y	H	L
B	A	E	T	I	K	C	U	E	T	O	U	D	B	T	A
R	F	U	Y	L	N	I	R	O	C	N	I	A	O	A	R
H	T	A	T	W	U	D	N	E	C	Y	C	N	L	H	J
H	Y	U	N	L	R	S	A	A	T	C	I	A	G	P	T
U	C	T	C	I	S	A	U	H	B	J	A	L	I	E	R
R	I	G	A	P	A	D	L	N	C	I	A	N	O	I	R
S	N	H	D	T	T	S	I	T	O	E	R	R	N	P	I
D	P	O	C	T	O	R	S	A	A	C	M	K	Y	A	I
C	A	R	T	T	I	S	T	I	T	D	W	I	T	T	P

TWISTED tip: Look for uncommon letters from the word list, such as J.

ACCOUNTANT
ACTOR
ARCHITECT
ARTIST
AUTHOR
BANKER
BUILDER
CASHIER
CONSULTANT
DOCTOR
ELECTRICIAN
HAIRDRESSER
JOURNALIST
LAWYER
MECHANIC
PLUMBER
POLICE OFFICER
SECRETARY
SINGER
TEACHER

....

83. LITTLE CLUES

What's the TWIST?

The names of 20 **flowers** are hidden in the grid. They may be written forwards or backwards in any direction, including diagonally.

Work out what the flowers are with the help of the initial letters given. The initials are listed alphabetically, which should help when there is more than one entry starting with the same letter.

TWISTED tip: There are three four-letter flowers and three five-letter flowers.

A S S I A I S E E R F O E N M O
S Y E L V I S P R T O L O I U R
E S F I O P O E R E T I R E M A
A I G L V P W E N E L I I A E A
I A Y O P O V V L E S C M O H I
R D N Y L O P O D L A A A R T L
E W O F L R I N O R R P I A N I
S D N C E V A O N Y A A N C A L
O U A W A D I A L A E Y O L S Y
S N T O I D T L R P E R G N Y D
W O P O L I I E T G S H E N R I
R F U R O S B E E S O R B I H H
N N A N E R E U I Y A O I E C C
R C A H E W S N I S E E P S L R
A L G G S C O R N F L O W E R O
I L I D O F F A D T P E O N Y L

A..
B..
C..
C..
C..
C..
D..
D..
D..
F..
G..
I..
L..
O..
P..
P..
R..
S..
S......................P...................
V..

84. SECRET WORDS

What's the TWIST?

Find each of the listed words in the grid. They may be written forwards or backwards in any direction, including diagonally.

Each entry in the word list contains at least one concealed **musical syllable** from the set DO, RE, MI, FA, SO, LA, TI; for example WINDFALL contains a hidden FA. Delete the hidden musical syllables from the words when searching for them in the grid. So for WINDFALL search for WINDLL.

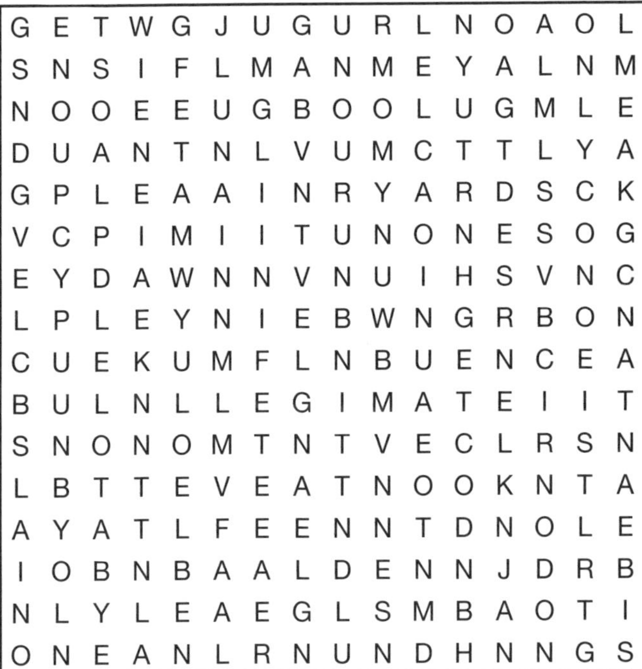

ABBREVIATES
BACKDOOR
COSTUMIER
DEFAULT
ENDORSED
FLOTATION
GLEAMING
HERESY
INEFFABLE
JUGULAR
LEGITIMATE
MONSOONS
NOVELLA
OVERCOMING
PREPAYMENT
TROUBLESOME
UNISON
VILLAIN
WINDFALL
YARDSTICK

TWISTED tip: Use the given list of musical notes to help simplify your search.

85. EMPTY INSIDE

What's the TWIST?

Find each of the listed **natural disaster** themed words and phrases in the grid. They may be written forwards or backwards in any direction, including diagonally.

Fill in the 36 blank squares in the centre of the grid as you place the entries.

H	I	M	U	P	P	N	D	I	G	O	A	Y	E	O	E
E	D	O	O	L	F	C	O	O	C	O	L	K	A	P	D
W	O	D	A	N	R	O	T	R	D	O	E	D	D	L	R
L	L	G	L	N	S	S	G	T	N	D	D	B	L	C	U
E	U	C	M	E	U	O	B	T	I	E	C	A	H	A	C
E	R	H	Y	N							F	U	I	U	F
E	Y	I	A	C							R	I	B	I	E
L	H	M	F	Z							P	A	U	E	N
E	I	N	Z	D							W	M	S	A	A
E	R	A	V	A							S	T	H	V	M
A	R	O	L	M							S	R	F	I	S
D	T	I	D	W	O	N	W	E	O	E	R	E	I	Y	R
H	A	H	A	A	E	E	W	R	P	M	E	A	R	E	R
P	I	V	O	Q	Y	E	M	M	T	B	V	A	E	E	D
D	E	F	A	M	I	N	E	O	Y	H	H	L	N	N	Y
H	P	P	N	D	O	T	Y	P	H	O	O	N	R	I	D

TWISTED tip: As there are no especially long entries in this puzzle, try cycling through each of the listed words a few times until you can be sure where each one is placed.

AVALANCHE
BLIZZARD
BUSH FIRE
CYCLONE
EARTHQUAKE
FAMINE
FLOOD
HEATWAVE
HURRICANE
LANDSLIDE
METEORITE
MONSOON
PLAGUE
STORM
TEMPEST
TORNADO
TSUNAMI
TYPHOON
WHIRLWIND
WILDFIRE

86. CROSS WORDS

What's the TWIST?

Find each of the listed words in the grid.

Each entry in the grid is cross-shaped – either X or +. The letter at the centre of each cross-shape (N in this case) is used twice. All entries in the grid read horizontally from left to right for the first half of the word, then from top to bottom for the second half.

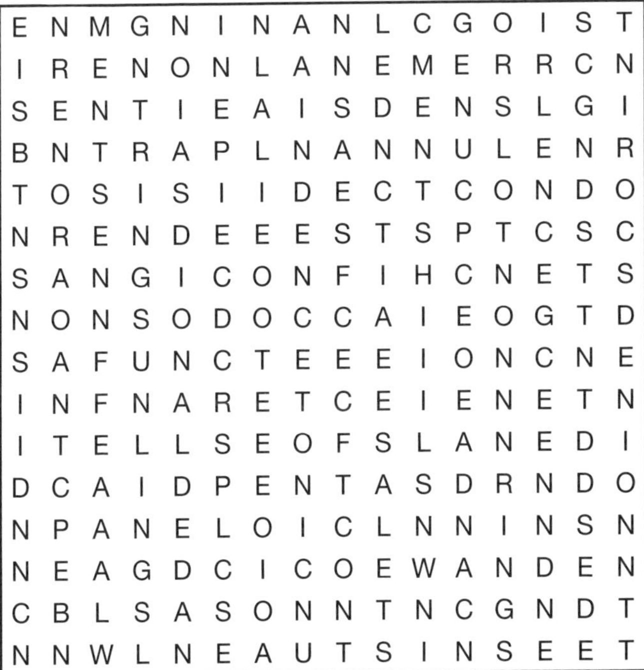

E N M G N I N A N L C G O I S T
I R E N O N L A N E M E R R C N
S E N T I E A I S D E N S L G I
B N T R A P L N A N N U L E N R
T O S I S I I D E C T C O N D O
N R E N D E E E S T S P T C S C
S A N G I C O N F I H C N E T S
N O N S O D O C C A I E O G T D
S A F U N C T E E E I O N C N E
I N F N A R E T C E I E N E T N
I T E L L S E O F S L A N E D I
D C A I D P E N T A S D R N D O
N P A N E L O I C L N N I N S N
N E A G D C I C O E W A N D E N
C B L S A S O N N T N C G N D T
N N W L N E A U T S I N S E E T

ANNULMENTS
ANOINT
BANDSTANDS
CONDOLENCE
CONFERENCE
CONFIDENCE
CONSCIENCE
ERRORS
FUNCTIONAL
INFANT
INLAND
INSANE
LENGTHENED
ONLINE
PANELLINGS
PENTATONIC
RENDERINGS
SANCTIONED
SENTIMENTS
WANDERINGS

TWISTED tip: The first letter to be used in the top row of the grid is M.

What's the TWIST?

Find each of the listed **spiral** themed words and phrases in the grid.

Each entry in the grid is found in the shape of a clockwise spiral, although the entry may read either from the centre of the spiral to the outside or from the outside of the spiral to the centre. One entry is marked as an example.

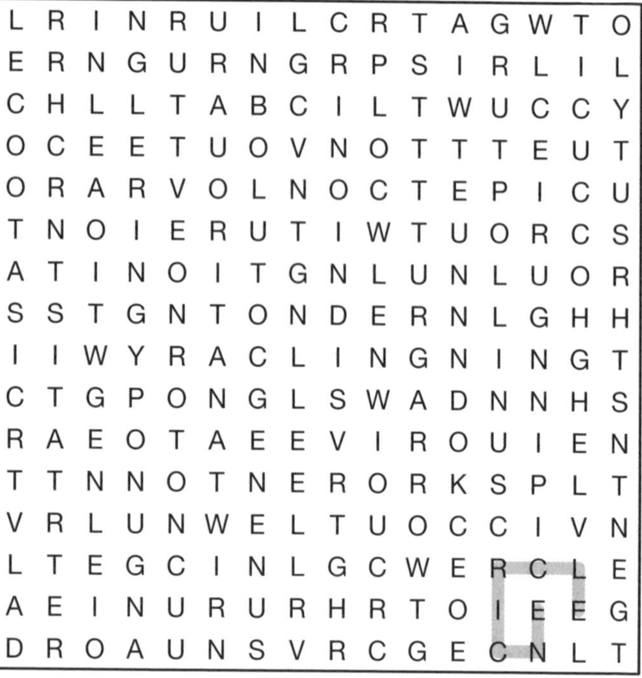

ABOUT-TURN
CIRCLING
COCHLEAR
CONVOLUTION
CORKSCREW
CURLICUE
~~ENCIRCLE~~
ENTANGLE
ENTWINE
GYRATION
PIROUETTE
PLOT TWIST
REVOLUTION
ROTATION
SCROLLING THROUGH
SPINNING AROUND
SWIVELLING
TURNING
TWISTING
WINDING RULE

TWISTED tip: Spirals always wind as tightly as possible around the central first letter.

88. SYMBOLIC

What's the TWIST?

Find each of the listed words and phrases in the grid. They may be written forwards or backwards in any direction, including diagonally.

Each word and phrase listed contains a shape; for example, CROP CIRCLE contains a CIRCLE. Replace the shapes with their corresponding pictorial form when searching for them in the grid. So for CROP CIRCLE search for CROP●.

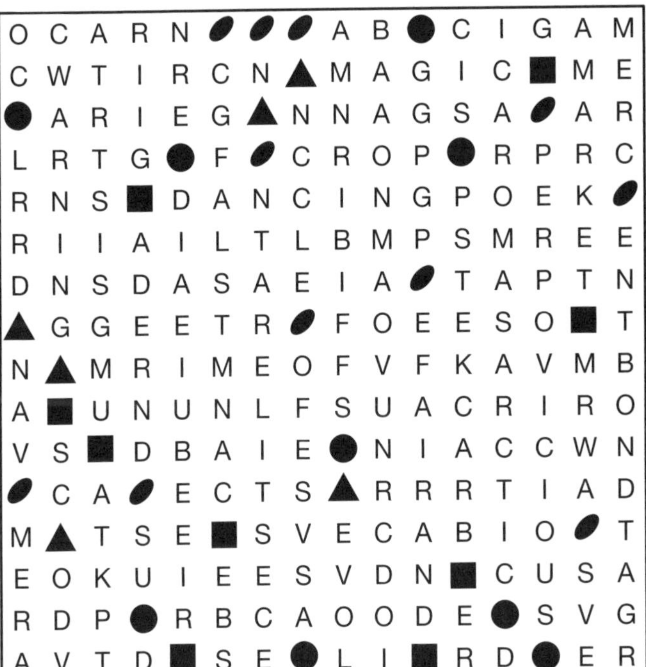

TWISTED tip: When the shape comes at the start or end of a word or phrase, search for the rest of the entry as usual then check that the shape is in the right place.

ARCTIC CIRCLE
BERMUDA TRIANGLE
COVALENT BOND
CROP CIRCLE
DRESS CIRCLE
FAIR AND SQUARE
LATIN SQUARE
LOVE TRIANGLE
MAGIC CIRCLE
MAGIC SQUARE
MARKET SQUARE
OVAL OFFICE
REMOVAL VAN
SEAL OF APPROVAL
SET SQUARE
SQUARE BRACKETS
SQUARE DANCING
SQUARE MEAL
VICIOUS CIRCLE
WARNING TRIANGLE

89. VOWELLESS

What's the TWIST?

Find each of the listed words and phrases in the grid. They may be written forwards or backwards in any direction, including diagonally.

Ignore all vowels (in this case they are all the letter O) in the words and phrases when searching in the grid. So for COWBOY BOOTS search or CWBYBTS.

TWISTED tip: With vowels deleted, relatively uncommon letters appear more frequently in this puzzle than in a standard word search grid.

C	C	R	Y	S	W	H	P	M	R	M	H	C	M	M	T
D	R	L	W	L	C	M	R	H	L	T	S	P	P	L	S
M	M	R	D	T	P	F	R	G	T	P	M	H	H	C	C
M	N	N	T	G	N	N	N	L	P	S	R	C	W	T	K
T	W	N	T	W	N	D	M	L	H	D	H	T	L	L	B
R	W	Z	L	P	N	M	C	F	T	C	R	T	Z	K	Z
L	B	L	G	T	M	T	M	T	L	S	S	T	G	N	D
K	F	C	L	M	S	M	H	C	F	D	T	L	D	M	W
P	Z	G	L	H	R	T	F	B	S	L	C	F	D	R	P
N	Y	S	M	N	L	R	B	S	S	S	F	N	S	H	B
K	N	N	M	K	P	S	K	Y	S	D	B	P	T	F	F
W	M	M	D	L	F	L	D	C	B	C	R	F	T	R	K
T	C	W	F	S	D	C	H	M	W	W	K	W	L	C	L
L	N	G	D	G	N	L	C	T	F	T	C	B	F	R	F
N	D	Y	K	T	B	L	M	T	R	R	R	D	K	K	R
C	N	S	K	K	L	C	F	R	N	F	B	R	F	H	B

BOOK OF WORDS
COMMON GOOD
COMMON ROOM
COOKBOOK
COTTON WOOL
COWBOY BOOTS
DOOR TO DOOR
FLOOD CONTROL
FOLLOW ON FROM
FOOLPROOF
FOOTSTOOL
GOOD LOOKS
LOCOMOTOR
LOOK DOWN ON
MONOPOLY
ODONTOLOGY
PHOTO SHOOT
PROTOZOON
SCHOOLBOOK
SCHOOL ROOM

90. WRAPAROUND

What's the TWIST?

Find each of the listed **fashion designers** in the grid. They may be written forwards or backwards in any direction, including diagonally.

Entries can wrap around from one edge of the grid to the other, so imagine that the grid repeats immediately on all sides. Names that wrap around continue on the opposite side to correspond with where they would be on the repeated grid.

TWISTED tip: Very few of the words in this puzzle are placed in the centre of the grid.

ARMANI
BANKS
BLASS
CHANEL
CONRAN
DIOR
GALLIANO
GAULTIER
GIVENCHY
GUCCI
KLEIN
LACROIX
LAGERFELD
LAROCHE
LAUREN
RICCI
TARLAZZI
VALENTINO
VERSACE
WESTWOOD

91. LEFTOVER LETTERS

What's the TWIST?

Find each of the listed **inventors** in the grid. They may be written forwards or backwards in any direction, including diagonally.

Each entry in the grid includes one extra letter (not shown in the word list). Make a note of the extra letter beside the corresponding name in the list. Then use the letters to spell out a related phrase in the space at the bottom of the page.

TWISTED tip: Search for a pair of adjacent letters from a listed word. If they aren't in the grid, every other pair of adjacent letters from that word must be.

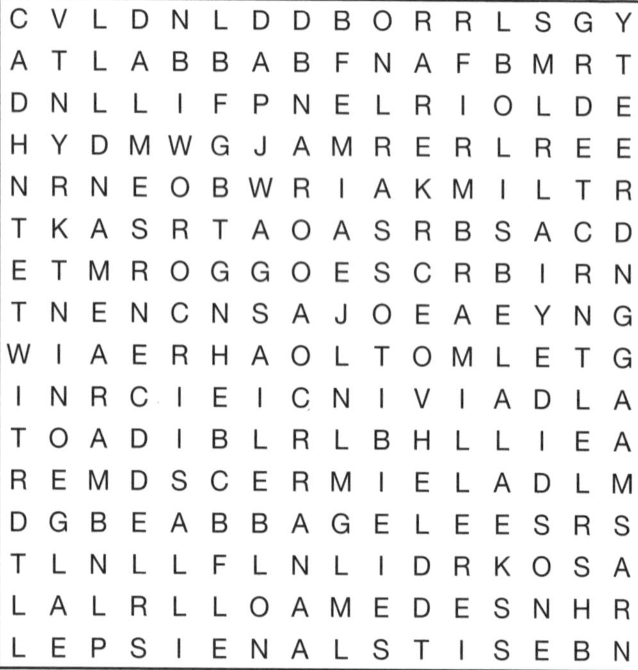

ANDERSON
ARCHIMEDES
BABBAGE
BELL
BERNERS-LEE
BRAILLE
DA VINCI
DYSON
EDISON
FLEMING
FORD
GALILEO
JOBS
LAMARR
MORSE
NEWTON
NOBEL
PASCAL
TESLA
WATT

....

92. LITTLE CLUES

What's the TWIST?

The names of 20 **flavours** are hidden in the grid. They may be written forwards or backwards in any direction, including diagonally.

Work out what the flavours are with the help of the initial letters given. The initials are listed alphabetically, which should help when there is more than one entry starting with the same letter.

B	R	A	G	E	M	I	L	N	T	E	R	L	C	L	G
V	E	G	N	A	R	O	C	N	O	E	Y	N	Q	I	I
A	N	N	O	M	E	L	N	N	D	M	E	E	I	Q	I
N	A	U	A	L	L	L	M	N	E	L	A	S	N	U	E
I	T	N	I	C	M	O	E	R	C	T	E	N	M	O	O
L	B	R	D	L	H	V	R	A	M	I	N	T	N	R	H
L	L	A	N	E	A	O	E	A	H	N	E	N	N	I	E
A	A	E	N	L	E	R	C	M	A	P	L	E	N	C	C
N	O	A	M	A	T	S	L	O	O	I	O	L	C	E	A
N	R	E	C	A	N	L	I	E	L	R	T	R	E	V	P
N	Y	G	I	V	R	A	A	N	N	A	L	M	R	N	P
Y	R	R	E	H	C	A	O	T	A	A	T	A	A	U	L
A	P	N	E	P	L	L	C	V	I	O	M	E	E	T	E
N	I	R	O	S	E	P	E	T	A	L	S	C	C	M	E
T	L	S	A	S	I	P	E	P	P	E	R	L	A	E	A
M	U	L	E	M	C	O	Y	R	Q	A	T	L	D	G	C

A............................ H............................ N............................
A............................ L............................ O............................
B............................ L............................ P............................
C............................ L............................ R.................P............
C............................ L............................ T............................
C............................ M............................ V............................
C............................ M............................

TWISTED tip: One of the four C-words is CHERRY and one of the L-words is LIME.

93. CROSS WORDS

What's the TWIST?

Find each of the listed words in the grid.

Each entry in the grid is cross-shaped – either X or +. The letter at the centre of each cross-shape (O in this case) is used twice. All entries in the grid read horizontally from left to right for the first half of the word, then from top to bottom for the second half.

TWISTED tip: There are so many Os in this puzzle that it isn't helpful to look for them until you find the rest of a word.

C H A O A O S L R H I H C O O N
B O O U T O O G A R W A O L B G
S O O B D I O L O D C D E O N T
O W R A O U O F D T O T O G L W
W B O R T I O N I L T D B Y R O
N R W R V I B L S O I N N A A D
B O S Y D O O T P R O B A D O K
M P O I N B G N R R N T R O U B
S S N D A G O R S O S L T U Q I
K A O W N O N O O P T Y O R O D
O G R O U N C R N R I O L N M O
D L I R B O N C Q U O T A C O M
F O L K O O O W I N N U B T N Q
D W L N B C N N U R S N D O C O
O L O L O V L G H O R R U R B N
T L P T N S L O G R R V R I R E

ABOLITIONS
BONBON
BOOHOO
BORROW
BROADSWORD
COCOON
COMMON
DEONTOLOGY
DOCTOR
FOLLOW
FORGOT
GORGON
GROUNDWORK
HORROR
LOLLOP
POISON
PROBATIONS
QUOTATIONS
TROUBADOUR
VIOLATIONS

94. LITTLE CLUES

What's the TWIST?

The names of 20 **types of educator** are hidden in the grid. They may be written forwards or backwards in any direction, including diagonally.

Work out what the words are with the help of the initial letters given. The initials are listed alphabetically, which should help when there is more than one entry starting with the same letter.

S	R	R	E	D	A	E	R	U	P	H	E	E	A	C	U
R	S	E	U	E	N	R	L	D	R	E	H	C	A	E	T
R	I	E	C	R	F	C	T	N	E	D	I	S	E	R	P
R	E	N	R	O	H	R	L	A	P	I	C	N	I	R	P
W	R	S	S	T	A	L	L	E	C	T	U	R	E	R	R
N	M	O	I	T	S	C	E	R	D	R	O	N	R	H	N
H	R	O	L	V	R	I	H	C	O	H	I	C	O	R	D
R	E	F	O	L	D	U	M	O	N	T	C	R	L	P	L
O	R	A	I	E	E	A	C	D	E	R	P	E	L	R	G
T	T	I	D	E	W	C	E	T	A	U	R	S	E	O	O
N	O	U	D	M	H	O	N	D	O	E	T	R	S	F	V
E	O	R	T	L	A	S	L	A	L	R	H	N	N	E	E
M	R	S	R	O	L	S	C	L	H	E	I	L	U	S	R
C	E	A	N	T	R	P	T	L	E	C	N	A	O	S	N
D	E	A	N	O	C	R	E	E	R	F	A	T	C	O	O
N	L	H	T	R	A	I	N	E	R	O	D	R	E	R	R

A...
C...
C...
C...
D...
D...
F...

G...
H...
H...
I...
L...
M...
P...

P...
P...
R...
T...
T...
T...

TWISTED tip: Both of the H words start with the same five letters.

95. WRAPAROUND

What's the TWIST?

Find each of the listed **snooker** themed words in the grid. They may be written forwards or backwards in any direction, including diagonally.

Entries can wrap around from one edge of the grid to the other, so imagine that the grid repeats immediately on all sides. Words that wrap around continue on the opposite side to correspond with where they would be on the repeated grid.

O	B	R	L	B	E	E	C	N	F	S	E	L	B	W	S
O	N	E	A	S	R	T	O	S	T	K	L	K	I	E	R
A	R	G	D	G	C	I	E	N	A	U	C	L	N	N	L
L	S	C	E	U	S	H	D	U	B	A	R	I	E	H	I
F	E	R	R	N	L	W	I	G	L	O	W	Y	L	W	C
V	E	G	E	E	E	L	E	B	E	B	W	E	E	U	R
W	R	T	C	D	S	M	E	R	W	W	U	Y	T	O	T
T	X	S	O	E	I	L	A	U	V	S	T	W	R	E	Y
E	S	K	I	E	E	P	E	R	R	E	E	L	T	W	R
B	L	F	Y	R	Y	T	S	N	F	E	W	B	I	T	E
A	I	L	B	F	P	R	N	A	N	N	S	F	U	B	Y
E	E	F	O	W	S	T	S	S	C	E	E	V	T	B	H
B	H	U	L	W	L	T	R	E	S	L	F	I	E	C	B
T	L	B	E	B	T	H	U	T	C	V	S	E	E	B	L
E	N	L	T	O	N	C	E	N	E	P	E	T	M	D	G
C	R	X	A	D	W	Y	E	F	I	M	S	E	T	D	L

BALL
BLACK
BLUE
BRIDGE
CENTURY
CHALK
CUE
EXTENSION
FOUL
FRAME
GREEN
SAFETY
SCREW
SPIDER
SPIN
STUN
SWERVE
TABLE
WHITE
YELLOW

TWISTED tip: About half of the words in this puzzle wrap around the edges of the grid.

96. OFF GRID

What's the TWIST?

Find each of the listed **shapes** in the grid. They may be written either forwards or backwards in any direction, including diagonally.

The grid is roughly circular in shape, but otherwise solves in the same way as a standard word search.

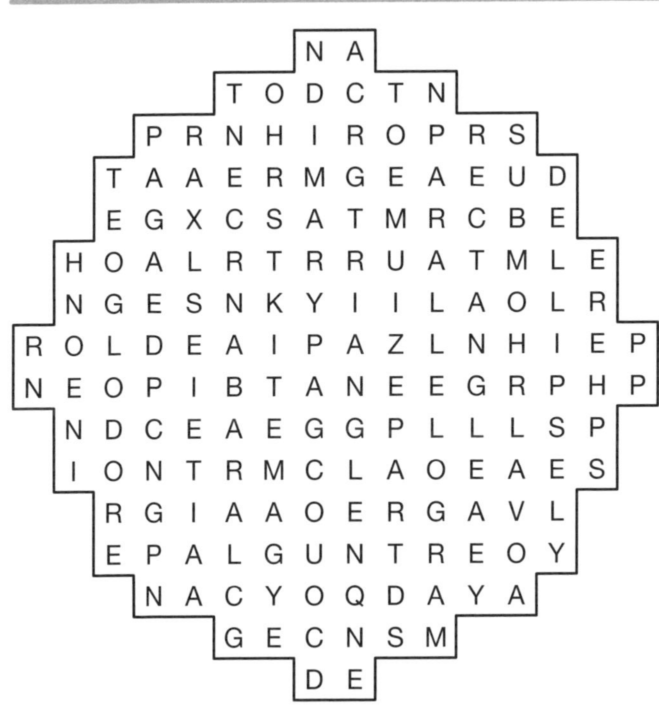

CIRCLE
CYLINDER
DECAGON
DIAMOND
ELLIPSE
HEART
HEXAGON
KITE
NONAGON
OCTAGON
OVAL
PARALLELOGRAM
PENTAGON
PYRAMID
RECTANGLE
RHOMBUS
SPHERE
SQUARE
TRAPEZIUM
TRIANGLE

TWISTED tip: Most of the letters in the grid will be used by at least one entry.

97. SYMBOLIC

What's the TWIST?

Find each of the listed words and phrases in the grid. They may be written forwards or backwards in any direction, including diagonally.

All occurrences of the word AT in the listed words and phrases have been replaced by an @ symbol in the grid. So for GRATIFICATION search for GR@IFIC@ION.

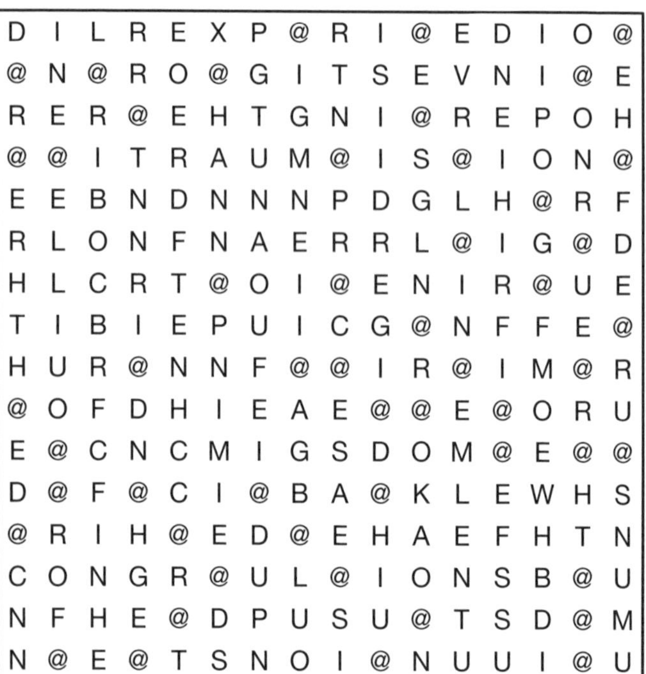

D	I	L	R	E	X	P	@	R	I	@	E	D	I	O	@
@	N	@	R	O	@	G	I	T	S	E	V	N	I	@	E
R	E	R	@	E	H	T	G	N	I	@	R	E	P	O	H
@	@	I	T	R	A	U	M	@	I	S	@	I	O	N	@
E	E	B	N	D	N	N	N	P	D	G	L	H	@	R	F
R	L	O	N	F	N	A	E	R	R	L	@	I	G	@	D
H	L	C	R	T	@	O	I	@	E	N	I	R	@	U	E
T	I	B	I	E	P	U	I	C	G	@	N	F	F	E	@
H	U	R	@	N	N	F	@	@	I	R	@	I	M	@	R
@	O	F	D	H	I	E	A	E	@	@	E	@	O	R	U
E	@	C	N	C	M	I	G	S	D	O	M	@	E	@	@
D	@	F	@	C	I	@	B	A	@	K	L	E	W	H	S
@	R	I	H	@	E	D	@	E	H	A	E	F	H	T	N
C	O	N	G	R	@	U	L	@	I	O	N	S	B	@	U
N	F	H	E	@	D	P	U	S	U	@	T	S	D	@	M
N	@	E	@	T	S	N	O	I	@	N	U	U	I	@	U

AT THAT RATE
BATH MAT
CONGRATULATIONS
DEATH THREAT
EXPATRIATED
FLOATATION
GRATIFICATION
HEAT DEATH
INFATUATED
INVESTIGATOR
KATABATIC
LATINATE
MATHEMATICIAN
NATION STATE
OPERATING THEATRE
RATATOUILLE
STATUS UPDATE
TRAUMATISATION
UNSATURATED FAT
WATERGATE

TWISTED tip: Look out for multiple occurrences of AT in many of the listed words and phrases.

98. SECRET WORDS

What's the TWIST?

Find each of the listed words and phrases in the grid. They may be written forwards or backwards in any direction, including diagonally.

Each entry in the word list contains at least one concealed **fish**; for example SQUIDGIEST contains a hidden SQUID. Delete the hidden fish from the words and phrases when searching for them in the grid. So for SQUIDGIEST search for GIEST.

M	E	S	N	N	R	E	R	E	I	I	T	R	S	U	T
E	W	N	E	M	E	D	L	R	R	T	T	A	E	E	A
N	R	I	T	T	I	D	P	E	E	E	E	B	E	P	R
B	H	S	L	R	Y	R	P	E	E	E	T	P	Y	E	P
T	O	P	S	L	D	P	E	F	H	N	N	N	R	I	L
T	S	H	L	C	I	A	R	E	E	O	W	E	E	N	N
P	R	O	T	H	R	A	R	N	I	N	N	N	R	E	A
Y	M	E	W	E	N	C	M	T	A	L	G	L	E	G	S
P	E	E	A	C	H	U	N	S	U	E	U	S	I	L	E
L	R	A	I	T	A	N	C	E	S	A	U	B	C	E	E
I	A	N	D	N	I	F	T	R	T	P	O	P	L	P	B
S	G	P	S	S	H	O	R	T	E	S	E	A	S	A	T
L	Y	T	Y	N	A	R	N	R	B	I	E	A	R	O	S
A	N	R	I	A	N	T	H	L	E	R	E	I	R	I	N
E	N	M	P	R	D	E	E	C	A	E	I	N	G	E	I
S	W	S	I	N	S	I	A	B	N	F	U	H	I	P	E

TWISTED tip: Even if you can't find all of the fish in the listed words, you can still use a process of elimination to identify them from the letters in the grid.

BARCODE
BRILLIANT
CARPENTER
EMBASSY
FREELANCING
HANDSHAKE
INSOLENT
MOLLYCODDLE
PAPER CHAIN
PERCHANCE
READABLE
RECLAMATION
SCHUBERT
SCRABBLE
SHORTEST ROUTE
SQUIDGIEST
SUPERHEROES
UNFORTUNATE
WHIPPERSNAPPER
WILLIAM SHAKESPEARE

99. LEFTOVER LETTERS

What's the TWIST?

Find each of the listed **mathematical** words in the grid. They may be written forwards or backwards in any direction, including diagonally.

Each entry in the grid includes one extra letter (not shown in the word list). Make a note of the extra letter beside the corresponding word in the list. Then use the letters to spell out a related phrase in the space at the bottom of the page.

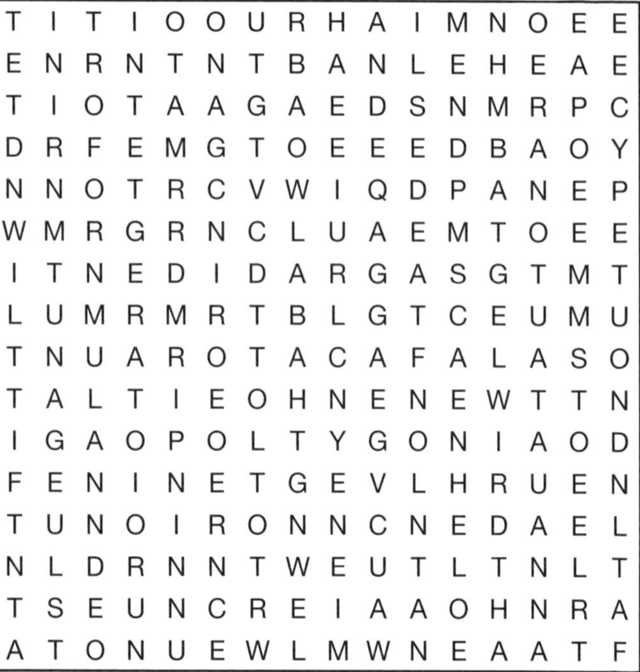

ALGEBRA
ANGLE
AREA
CONSTANT
DECIMAL
EQUATION
FACTOR
FORMULA
GRADIENT
INTEGER
LENGTH
MEAN
POLYGON
RATIO
SUM
TANGENT
TRIANGLE
UNITS
VOLUME
WIDTH

TWISTED tip: The hidden phrase refers to addition.

....

What's the TWIST?

Find each of the listed **twists and turns** themed words in the grid.

Each entry in the grid is found in the shape of a line with a single 90-degree bend in it, reading in any direction. One entry is marked as an example.

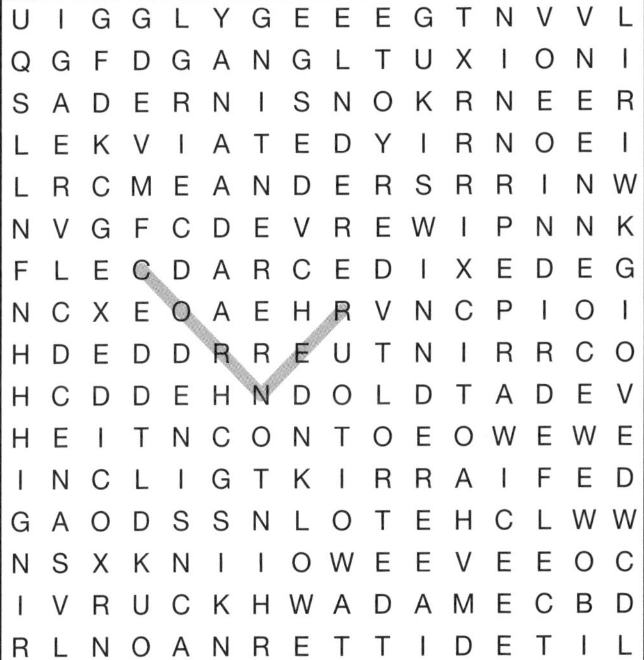

ANGLE
ARCHED
BOWED
CHAOTIC
CONTORTED
~~CORNER~~
CURVING
DEFLECTED
DEVIATED
FLEXED
HOOK
INCLINED
KINK
MEANDERED
SQUIGGLY
SWERVED
TURNING
TWIST
VEERED
WARPED

TWISTED tip: Remember to look for both straight and diagonal lines with bends.

101. CROSS WORDS

What's the TWIST?

Find each of the listed words and phrases in the grid.

Each entry in the grid is cross-shaped – either X or +. The letter at the centre of each cross-shape (T in this case) is used twice. All entries in the grid read horizontally from left to right for the first half of the word or phrase, then from top to bottom for the second half.

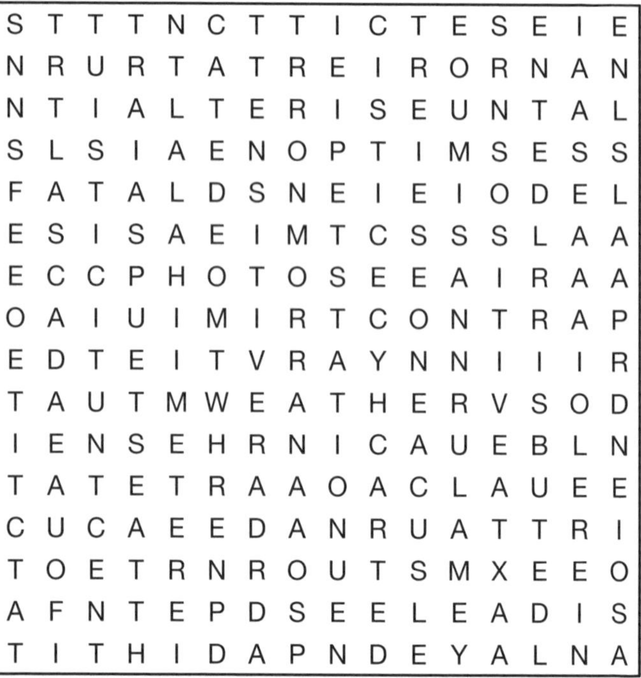

S	T	T	T	N	C	T	T	I	C	T	E	S	E	I	E
N	R	U	R	T	A	T	R	E	I	R	O	R	N	A	N
N	T	I	A	L	T	E	R	I	S	E	U	N	T	A	L
S	L	S	I	A	E	N	O	P	T	I	M	S	E	S	S
F	A	T	A	L	D	S	N	E	I	E	I	O	D	E	L
E	S	I	S	A	E	I	M	T	C	S	S	S	L	A	A
E	C	C	P	H	O	T	O	S	E	E	A	I	R	A	A
O	A	I	U	I	M	I	R	T	C	O	N	T	R	A	P
E	D	T	E	I	T	V	R	A	Y	N	N	I	I	I	R
T	A	U	T	M	W	E	A	T	H	E	R	V	S	O	D
I	E	N	S	E	H	R	N	I	C	A	U	E	B	L	N
T	A	T	E	T	R	A	A	O	A	C	L	A	U	E	E
C	U	C	A	E	E	D	A	N	R	U	A	T	T	R	I
T	O	E	T	R	N	R	O	U	T	S	M	X	E	E	O
A	F	N	T	E	P	D	S	E	E	L	E	A	D	I	S
T	I	T	H	I	D	A	P	N	D	E	Y	A	L	N	A

ALTERCATED
ANTIMATTER
ATTRIBUTED
CENTRALISATION
CONTRAPOSITIVE
EXTENUATES
FATALISTIC
FEATHER DUSTERS
INTERACTED
METEORITES
OPTIMISTIC
OUTSMARTED
PETULANTLY
PHOTOSENSITIVE
STARTS
STILTS
STUNTS
TETRAMETER
UNTALENTED
WEATHER STATION

TWISTED tip: The long words and phrases in this puzzle make it relatively easy to solve.

102. SYMBOLIC

What's the TWIST?

Find each of the listed words and phrases in the grid. They may be written forwards or backwards in any direction, including diagonally.

All occurences of the word STAR in the listed words and phrases have been replaced a ★ symbol in the grid. So for FIRE STARTER search for FIRE★TER.

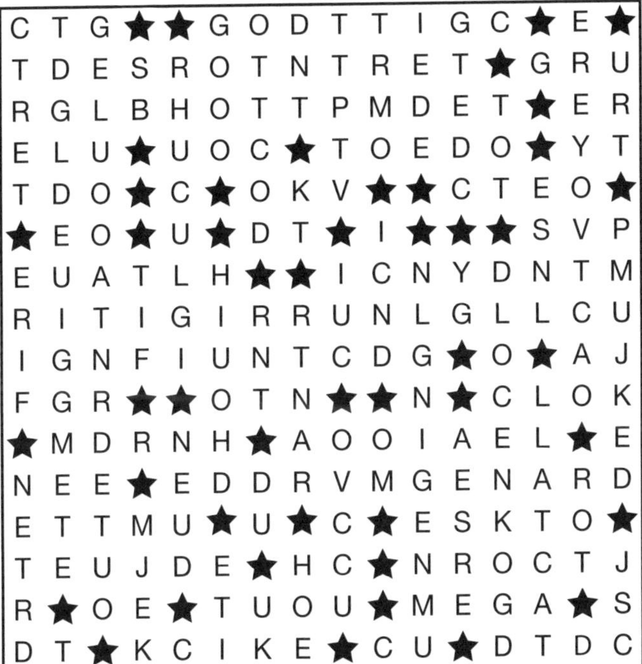

ALL-STAR
BUSTARD
COLD START
CORNSTARCH
CO-STAR
CUT THE MUSTARD
CUSTARD
DASTARDLY
EUROSTAR
FIRE STARTER
JUMP-START
KICK-START
MEGASTARS
NON-STARTER
OUTSTARE
RESTARTED
ROCKSTAR
SHOOTING STAR
STARLING
STARVING

TWISTED tip: Start with the longest words and phrases, resisting the temptation to search for star symbols in the grid.

103. LITTLE CLUES

What's the TWIST?

The names of 20 **sports** are hidden in the grid. They may be written forwards or backwards in any direction, including diagonally.

Work out what the sports are with the help of the initial letters given. The initials are listed alphabetically, which should help when there is more than one entry starting with the same letter.

<table>
<tr><td>I</td><td>I</td><td>L</td><td>G</td><td>C</td><td>A</td><td>N</td><td>O</td><td>E</td><td>I</td><td>N</td><td>G</td><td>S</td><td>I</td><td>C</td><td>A</td></tr>
<tr><td>O</td><td>T</td><td>R</td><td>I</td><td>A</td><td>T</td><td>H</td><td>L</td><td>O</td><td>N</td><td>D</td><td>N</td><td>J</td><td>N</td><td>Y</td><td>R</td></tr>
<tr><td>S</td><td>N</td><td>B</td><td>T</td><td>T</td><td>O</td><td>L</td><td>L</td><td>A</td><td>B</td><td>D</td><td>N</td><td>A</td><td>H</td><td>C</td><td>C</td></tr>
<tr><td>W</td><td>O</td><td>A</td><td>S</td><td>A</td><td>Y</td><td>O</td><td>S</td><td>D</td><td>G</td><td>A</td><td>E</td><td>C</td><td>A</td><td>L</td><td>H</td></tr>
<tr><td>T</td><td>E</td><td>N</td><td>N</td><td>G</td><td>S</td><td>A</td><td>B</td><td>Y</td><td>S</td><td>C</td><td>T</td><td>L</td><td>C</td><td>I</td><td>E</td></tr>
<tr><td>I</td><td>G</td><td>I</td><td>T</td><td>Y</td><td>I</td><td>C</td><td>M</td><td>H</td><td>B</td><td>N</td><td>L</td><td>V</td><td>O</td><td>N</td><td>R</td></tr>
<tr><td>S</td><td>C</td><td>B</td><td>G</td><td>L</td><td>M</td><td>N</td><td>O</td><td>A</td><td>G</td><td>A</td><td>S</td><td>O</td><td>D</td><td>G</td><td>Y</td></tr>
<tr><td>N</td><td>U</td><td>I</td><td>I</td><td>H</td><td>A</td><td>O</td><td>D</td><td>I</td><td>B</td><td>N</td><td>I</td><td>L</td><td>U</td><td>G</td><td>Y</td></tr>
<tr><td>L</td><td>N</td><td>N</td><td>W</td><td>S</td><td>T</td><td>M</td><td>B</td><td>T</td><td>H</td><td>S</td><td>N</td><td>L</td><td>J</td><td>N</td><td>A</td></tr>
<tr><td>A</td><td>G</td><td>G</td><td>T</td><td>I</td><td>I</td><td>L</td><td>E</td><td>Y</td><td>W</td><td>S</td><td>N</td><td>E</td><td>F</td><td>I</td><td>J</td></tr>
<tr><td>I</td><td>I</td><td>I</td><td>N</td><td>N</td><td>A</td><td>K</td><td>I</td><td>I</td><td>S</td><td>K</td><td>E</td><td>Y</td><td>E</td><td>L</td><td>U</td></tr>
<tr><td>R</td><td>C</td><td>G</td><td>T</td><td>I</td><td>S</td><td>Y</td><td>M</td><td>F</td><td>R</td><td>T</td><td>T</td><td>B</td><td>N</td><td>T</td><td>M</td></tr>
<tr><td>S</td><td>G</td><td>O</td><td>X</td><td>A</td><td>V</td><td>M</td><td>O</td><td>O</td><td>T</td><td>M</td><td>L</td><td>A</td><td>C</td><td>S</td><td>P</td></tr>
<tr><td>V</td><td>N</td><td>E</td><td>B</td><td>T</td><td>I</td><td>I</td><td>N</td><td>H</td><td>R</td><td>I</td><td>N</td><td>L</td><td>I</td><td>E</td><td>I</td></tr>
<tr><td>X</td><td>T</td><td>I</td><td>I</td><td>N</td><td>B</td><td>I</td><td>D</td><td>N</td><td>B</td><td>C</td><td>N</td><td>L</td><td>N</td><td>R</td><td>N</td></tr>
<tr><td>L</td><td>N</td><td>I</td><td>G</td><td>B</td><td>O</td><td>X</td><td>I</td><td>N</td><td>G</td><td>M</td><td>M</td><td>G</td><td>G</td><td>W</td><td>G</td></tr>
</table>

A...
B...
B...
B...
C...
C...
D...
F...
G...
H...
J...
J...
S...
S...
S...
T...
T...
V...
W...
W...

TWISTED tip: Three of the sports end in -BALL.

104. LEFTOVER LETTERS

What's the TWIST?

Find each of the listed **medical** words and phrases in the grid. They may be written forwards or backwards in any direction, including diagonally.

Each entry in the grid includes one extra letter (not shown in the word list). Make a note of the extra letter beside the corresponding word or phrase in the list. Then use the letters to spell out a related phrase in the space at the bottom of the page.

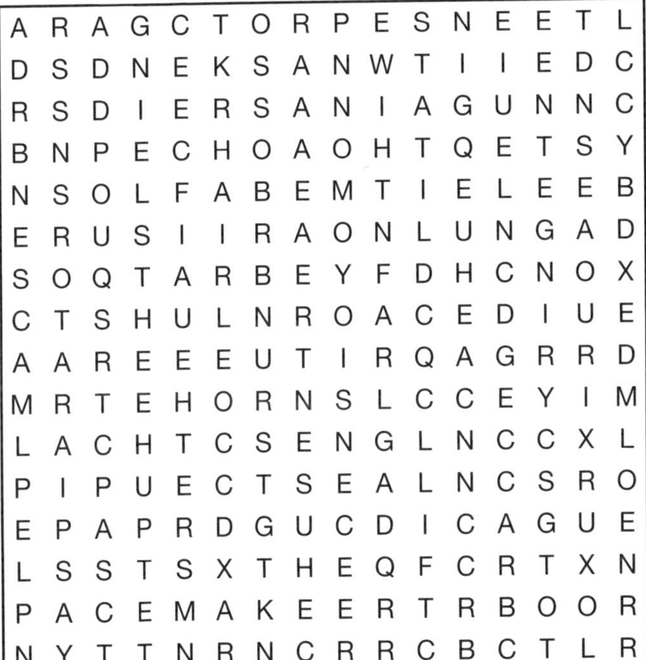

ASPIRATOR
BANDAGE
BRACE
CANNULA
CATHETER
CRUTCHES
DEFIBRILLATOR
FORCEPS
IRON LUNG
NEEDLE
OXYGEN MASK
PACEMAKER
SCALPEL
SLING
SPLINT
STRETCHER
SUTURE
SWAB
SYRINGE
TOURNIQUET

TWISTED tip: A good tip for most word search puzzles is to start with the longest entries.

....

105. SHAPED WORDS

What's the TWIST?

Find each of the listed double Z-words in the grid.

Each entry in the grid is found in the shape of a zigzag, reading in any horizontal, vertical or diagonal direction. One entry is marked as an example.

TWISTED tip: The zigzags in the grid are all regular; once they have 'zigged' one way and 'zagged' the other they then continue to 'zig' and 'zag' in exactly the same way for their entire length.

E S F J Z G I Z S E A Z A U Z A
D T A I Z Z B E S T Z R I Z Q B
H R Z Z P U I N E M N U A L S R
E G Z B Z Z Z Z L G A N E A S E
Z N I Y F U L E E L D Z L L Z I
Z Q S G M Z B M E Q H Z I A Z N
U I Z U O Z E O N T Z B I Z A A
Z Z S A L Z A M L E L R D G Z Z
Z L Z M E S R E A Z Z I E G A N
N B N E Z I D L L L Z I R N E Z
A L T L Z A Z Z A E R Z D Z N A
A H N I Z L U A Z I A Z I B M M
D A G D I U N A Z I I R E G R I
W Z Z U Z Z S N D P D M Z S E I
H I L I L I E E Z E I R Z U Z E
W D G N G I R L B L S E Z Q A S

BEDAZZLE
BLIZZARD
BUZZARD
DAZZLING
DIZZIER
DRIZZLE
EMBEZZLEMENT
FIZZIEST
FUZZINESS
~~GRIZZLED~~
JAZZY
MEZZALUNA
MOZZARELLA
NUZZLING
PIZZAZZ
PUZZLEMENT
QUIZZES
SIZZLING
SNAZZIER
WHIZZ

106. EMPTY INSIDE

What's the TWIST?

Find each of the listed **exclusion** themed words and phrases in the grid. They may be written forwards or backwards in any direction, including diagonally.

Fill in the 36 blank squares in the centre of the grid as you place the entries.

T	T	S	T	Y	T	T	S	S	E	C	L	U	D	E	A
E	G	T	S	R	A	H	T	E	X	C	L	U	D	E	B
E	E	Y	T	V	U	T	T	U	C	I	A	E	T	M	O
N	N	E	R	T	T	O	C	Y	O	B	A	A	A	S	T
E	R	P	O	T	S	C	A	S	M	W	I	R	T	T	M
S	A	U	Q	T							O	R	N	A	R
T	T	E	E	U							A	R	R	E	T
O	R	L	B	E							E	G	H	R	E
G	L	A	N	L							I	C	A	T	N
A	N	A	P	E							C	P	A	I	O
E	T	S	R	A							A	S	T	T	D
E	A	G	O	A	T	T	K	L	T	P	T	T	I	L	O
E	E	E	O	V	O	E	I	L	E	I	P	D	D	D	T
S	T	A	E	O	V	S	S	E	I	A	N	L	N	S	G
T	E	T	Z	Z	E	E	K	H	E	S	A	E	E	E	T
P	U	C	R	U	K	I	S	O	L	A	T	E	T	N	S

TWISTED tip: Entries that have more than six letters must use one or more of the given letters in the grid as well as occupying the empty heart of the puzzle.

ALIENATE
BLACKLIST
BOYCOTT
DISCONNECT
EXCLUDE
EXCOMMUNICATE
ISOLATE
KEEP APART
MARGINALISE
MAROON
OSTRACISE
QUARANTINE
REPUDIATE
SECLUDE
SEGREGATE
SEND TO COVENTRY
SET APART
SHUT OUT
THROW OUT
VOTE AGAINST

107. CROSS WORDS

What's the TWIST?

Find each of the listed words and phrases in the grid.

Each entry in the grid is cross-shaped – either **X** or **+**. The letter at the centre of each cross-shape is used twice. All entries in the grid read horizontally from left to right for the first half of the word or phrase, then from top to bottom for the second half.

TWISTED tip: Work out which will be the central letter of each entry; this will tell you which type of cross you are looking for.

```
E W T R E S E G G E W V F P L S
L R U G O B E N R N H S W R A L
E N R A P U A E C H I N A B P P
E E E R L R N T S B T S I L V E
T D D B O N I D S L E G R U N S
Y E L L O W W S L A T E R E S E
E R O E N R N W E C A N N E B N
R L W R R O P T E K E V R E E E
E C I S M A I D E E E C E C S N
H B E L R H N S R R D P U R P L
S R D S W U K G E I R S E A E R
W I S F I H O N A K O P E B E D
E U D E I N E C C R O D L O E H
C E S L D E O A R E D B L A C K
R U M E R A L O D A E K L R T L
R D R G A B Y D U S D D D D E D
```

BLACKBOARD
BLACKHEADS
BLUE GROUND
CHINA WHITE
CRESS GREEN
ENRAPTURED
GREENFIELD
GREENWEEDS
MAIDEN PINK
ORANGE BATS
PERSEVERED
PURPLE CRAB
RED-BLOODED
REDEEM
RED NOSE DAY
RED SEA
SILVER-BLUE
SLATE-BLACK
WHITE NOISE
YELLOW WARBLERS

108. WARPED VISION

What's the TWIST?

Find each of the listed **knot** themed words and phrases in the grid. They may be written forwards or backwards in any direction, including diagonally.

The rows and columns that make up the grid have been twisted, but you should still solve the puzzle as if they were perfectly straight.

F	S	H	K	B	P	C	E	O	E	D	W	L	E	U	L
N	A	U	S	N	E	W	B	E	E	I	T	B	S	R	A
L	W	P	A	E	A	E	L	B	U	O	D	L	E	C	V
U	A	S	N	A	M	H	S	I	L	G	N	E	A	E	C
A	O	A	A	A	I	O	S	H	R	R	S	R	L	C	L
B	N	C	E	L	I	O	W	P	I	N	R	N	B	O	I
I	L	I	R	N	W	A	V	S	E	I	S	M	E	E	N
K	L	H	T	O	P	P	U	E	C	E	U	U	R	R	C
I	A	H	I	S	C	R	S	K	R	H	H	W	A	F	H
M	W	U	T	T	G	H	B	A	T	H	I	S	U	T	H
O	E	A	H	E	C	E	E	U	I	N	A	E	Q	H	W
H	C	M	O	H	N	H	A	T	D	L	R	N	S	F	L
L	H	N	C	D	R	O	B	S	P	O	O	S	D	L	S
S	S	T	G	N	U	N	O	I	A	F	H	R	O	A	A
I	U	F	E	E	R	R	N	O	U	E	R	R	S	T	M
M	F	I	S	H	E	R	M	A	N	S	O	D	K	A	S

CARRICK BEND
CAT'S PAW
CLINCH
CROCHET
DOUBLE
ENGLISHMAN'S
FISHERMAN'S
FLAT
HITCH
MESH
OVERHAND
REEF
SAILOR'S
SHEEPSHANK
SQUARE
SURGEON'S
THUMB
TIE
WALL
WINDSOR

TWISTED tip: This puzzle is best taken slowly – look for a few entries, then take a break before continuing!

109. VOWELLESS

What's the TWIST?

Find each of the listed words in the grid. They may be written forwards or backwards in any direction, including diagonally.

Ignore all vowels (in this case every other letter) in the words when searching in the grid. So for FANATICAL search or FNTCL.

TWISTED tip: All of the listed words have nine letters including four vowels, so all will be five letters long in the grid.

T	F	F	T	V	T	R	N	T	N	C	P	Y	C	C	N
H	M	V	M	S	T	B	D	R	D	D	C	D	L	R	F
T	X	R	V	S	C	C	R	N	M	V	L	C	R	N	V
N	V	G	L	T	F	W	D	K	W	T	C	V	T	C	T
T	C	V	N	R	X	C	L	M	M	D	C	C	R	M	R
T	C	N	B	L	M	S	N	L	C	C	L	R	V	D	N
N	P	S	D	C	G	G	T	H	R	M	P	S	L	M	C
R	P	L	P	T	N	R	L	R	T	T	G	C	V	D	W
P	H	R	V	R	G	D	Y	L	N	R	M	L	R	R	D
N	L	D	L	R	Y	V	C	K	L	V	F	R	T	V	L
N	C	T	T	D	D	M	N	T	M	R	C	G	B	R	L
R	M	D	C	G	F	C	V	D	N	L	V	P	R	Y	C
L	G	N	R	L	L	S	L	V	F	L	N	D	C	N	L
T	R	R	T	R	R	R	T	D	D	R	C	C	P	R	S
T	T	D	M	S	S	D	R	T	M	R	D	N	T	F	T
V	P	M	S	R	N	C	S	C	N	D	R	P	S	M	D

BAREFACED
BAROMETER
CATAMARAN
CAVEWOMAN
DELIVERED
FANATICAL
FIGURINES
HEXAGONAL
HOLIDAYED
NAVIGATED
NOMINATES
PACEMAKER
PANORAMIC
POLITICAL
RELATIVES
RELEGATED
RENOVATED
RIDICULED
VALIDATES
VENERATES

110. LITTLE CLUES

What's the TWIST?

The names of 20 **musical instruments** are hidden in the grid. They may be written forwards or backwards in any direction, including diagonally.

Work out what the instruments are with the help of the initial letters given. The initials are listed alphabetically, which should help when there is more than one entry starting with the same letter.

```
A D N O L O C C I P T R I I T T
R F O M E E N O H P O X A S A M
E R O E P U N A T E C X L M R A
D R S A T E T O E R R E B D D T
R R S H O I T H B T U O H S H I
O S A A B N U E U M U M A N B M
C R B R N O R B N R O O P D O P
E A V P O O A O I I T R O E B A
R T I S I N L N H F R U T O T N
R I O I D A E D L H B A T A C I
H U L C R B N U O L C E L C T N
N G I H O A T O E L N N C C O B
O E N O C E N B R R O B E T I I
E R A R C N A D O M B C M R I R
S R T D A S E C D T O N E E F T
N O R G S E L G N A I R T I M N
```

A..
B..
C..
C..
D....................B....................
F..
F....................H....................

G..
H..
P..
P..
R..
S..
T..

T..
T..
T..
T..
T..
V..

TWISTED tip: Five of the instruments are from the brass section.

SOLUTIONS

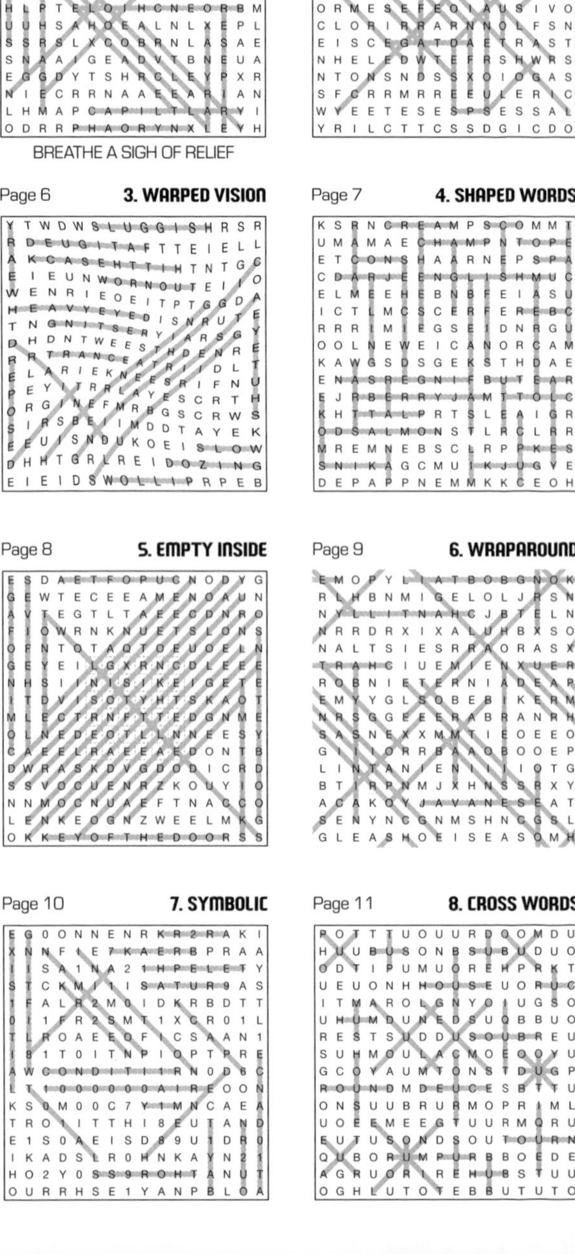
Page 4
1. LEFTOVER LETTERS
BREATHE A SIGH OF RELIEF
Page 5
2. SECRET WORDS
Page 6
3. WARPED VISION
Page 7
4. SHAPED WORDS
Page 8
5. EMPTY INSIDE
Page 9
6. WRAPAROUND
Page 10
7. SYMBOLIC
Page 11
8. CROSS WORDS

Page 12 **9. LEFTOVER LETTERS**

THE STRONG ARM OF THE LAW

Page 13 **10. LITTLE CLUES**

AQUAMARINE
BLACK
BLUE
BROWN
CREAM
GOLD
GREEN
INDIGO
LILAC
MAGENTA
OLIVE
ORANGE
PINK
RED
SILVER
TAN
TURQUOISE
VIOLET
WHITE
YELLOW

Page 14 **11. SECRET WORDS**

Page 15 **12. EMPTY INSIDE**

Page 16 **13. SHAPED WORDS**

Page 17 **14. THIS AND THAT**

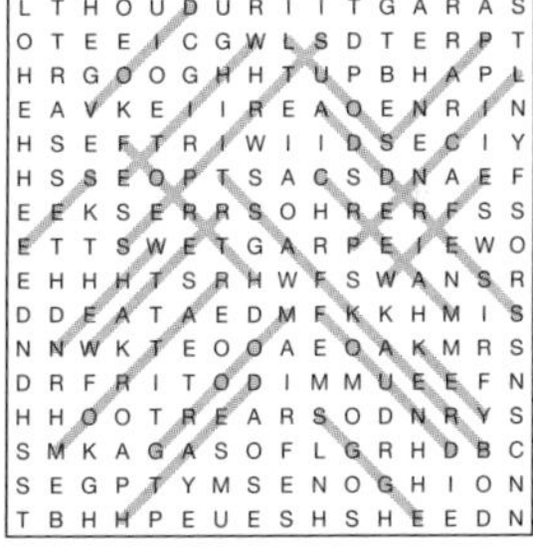

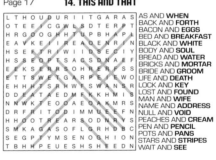

AS AND **WHEN**
BACK AND **FORTH**
BACON AND **EGGS**
BED AND **BREAKFAST**
BLACK AND **WHITE**
BODY AND **SOUL**
BREAD AND **WATER**
BRICKS AND **MORTAR**
BRIDE AND **GROOM**
LIFE AND **DEATH**
LOCK AND **KEY**
LOST AND **FOUND**
MAN AND **WIFE**
NAME AND **ADDRESS**
NULL AND **VOID**
PEACHES AND **CREAM**
PEN AND **PENCIL**
POTS AND **PANS**
STARS AND **STRIPES**
WAIT AND **SEE**

Page 18 **15. LEFTOVER LETTERS**

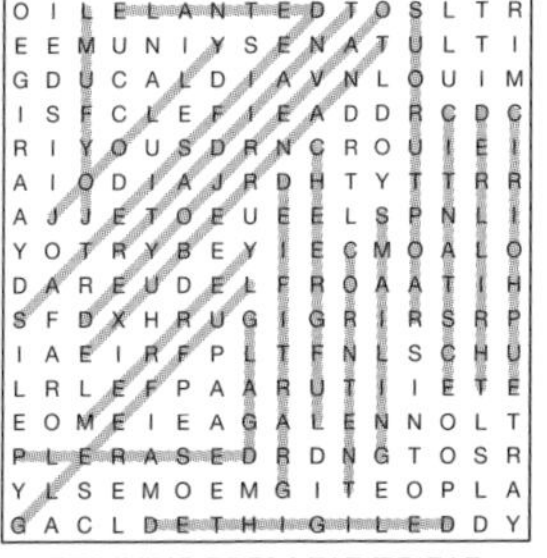

GRINNING FROM EAR TO EAR

Page 19 **16. LITTLE CLUES**

AMSTERDAM
ATHENS
BEIJING
BERLIN
BRUSSELS
BUDAPEST
CAIRO
CANBERRA
COPENHAGEN
DUBLIN
HELSINKI
LONDON
MADRID
MOSCOW
PARIS
ROME
SEOUL
STOCKHOLM
TOKYO
WASHINGTON DC

SOLUTIONS

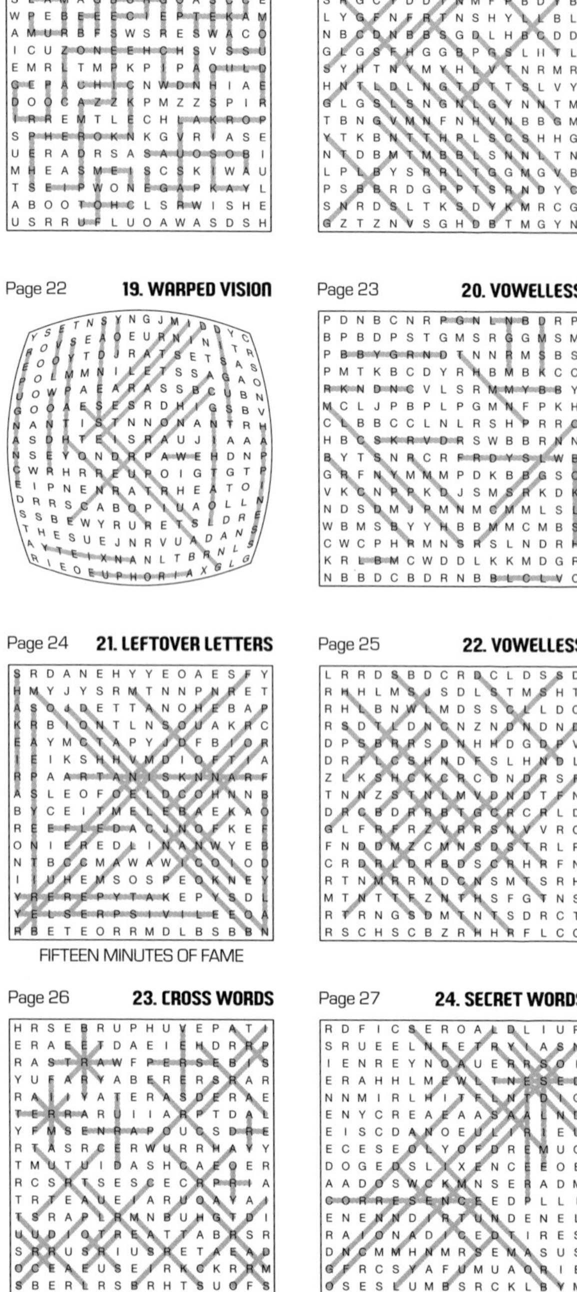
Page 20
17. SHAPED WORDS
Page 21
18. VOWELLESS
Page 22
19. WARPED VISION
Page 23
20. VOWELLESS
Page 24
21. LEFTOVER LETTERS
FIFTEEN MINUTES OF FAME
Page 25
22. VOWELLESS
Page 26
23. CROSS WORDS
Page 27
24. SECRET WORDS

Page 28 — 25. WRAPAROUND

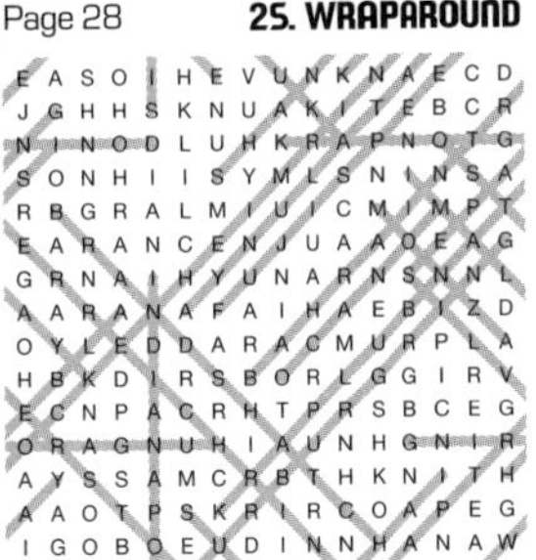

Page 29 — 26. LITTLE CLUES

AFGHANISTAN
ALGERIA
CAMBODIA
CHINA
DENMARK
ETHIOPIA
FINLAND
FRANCE
GAMBIA
IRAQ
LUXEMBOURG
MEXICO
NIGERIA
PORTUGAL
SINGAPORE
SPAIN
SWITZERLAND
THAILAND
UKRAINE
ZIMBABWE

Page 30 — 27. LEFTOVER LETTERS

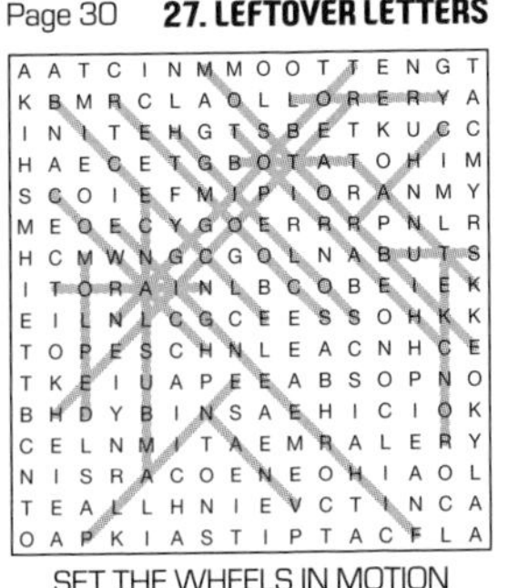

SET THE WHEELS IN MOTION

Page 31 — 28. CROSS WORDS

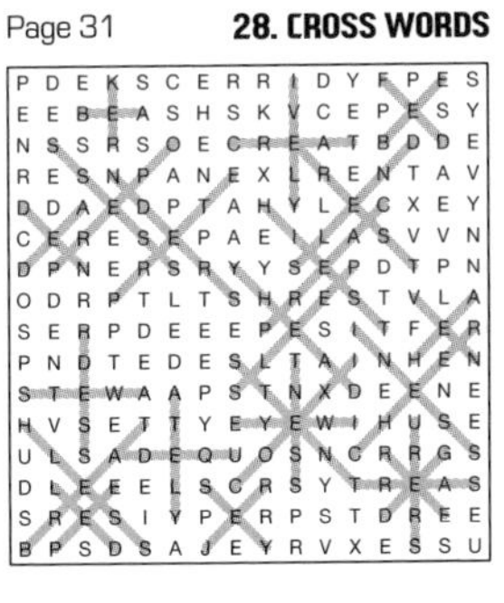

SOLUTIONS

Page 32 — 29. EMPTY INSIDE

Page 33 — 30. LITTLE CLUES

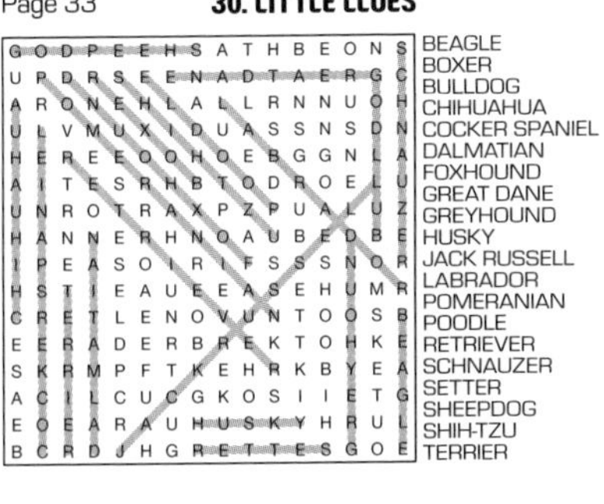

BEAGLE
BOXER
BULLDOG
CHIHUAHUA
COCKER SPANIEL
DALMATIAN
FOXHOUND
GREAT DANE
GREYHOUND
HUSKY
JACK RUSSELL
LABRADOR
POMERANIAN
POODLE
RETRIEVER
SCHNAUZER
SETTER
SHEEPDOG
SHIH-TZU
TERRIER

Page 34 — 31. SHAPED WORDS

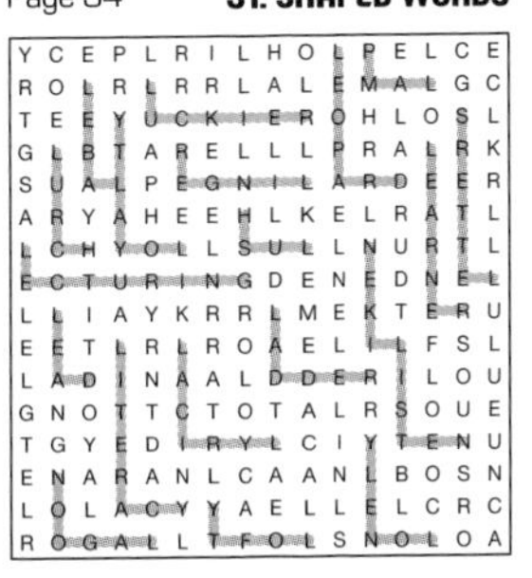

Page 35 — 32. THIS AND THAT

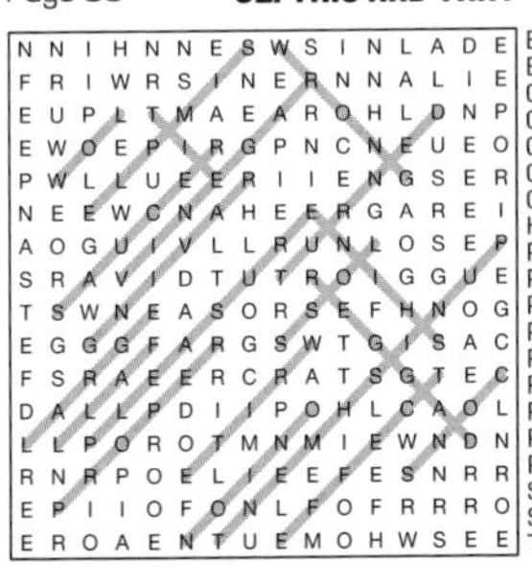

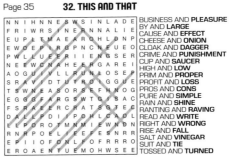

BUSINESS AND **PLEASURE**
BY AND **LARGE**
CAUSE AND **EFFECT**
CHEESE AND **ONION**
CLOAK AND **DAGGER**
CRIME AND **PUNISHMENT**
CUP AND **SAUCER**
HIGH AND **LOW**
PRIM AND **PROPER**
PROFIT AND **LOSS**
PROS AND **CONS**
PURE AND **SIMPLE**
RAIN AND **SHINE**
RANTING AND **RAVING**
READ AND **WRITE**
RIGHT AND **WRONG**
RISE AND **FALL**
SALT AND **VINEGAR**
SUIT AND **TIE**
TOSSED AND **TURNED**

Page 36 **33. WRAPAROUND**

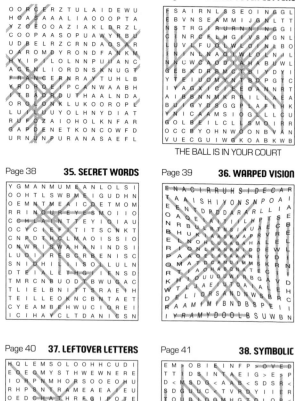

Page 37 **34. LEFTOVER LETTERS**

THE BALL IS IN YOUR COURT

Page 38 **35. SECRET WORDS**

Page 39 **36. WARPED VISION**

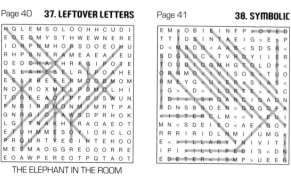

Page 40 **37. LEFTOVER LETTERS**

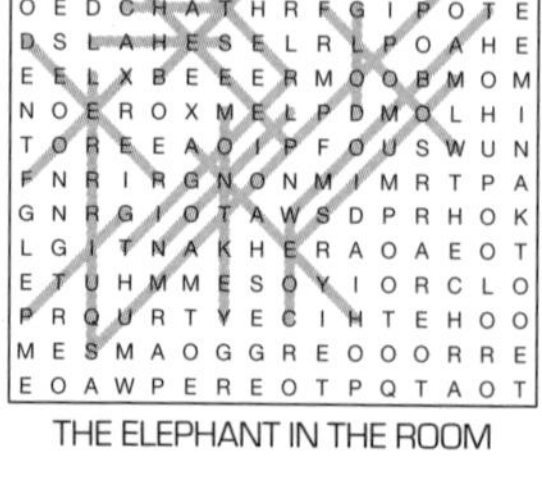

THE ELEPHANT IN THE ROOM

Page 41 **38. SYMBOLIC**

Page 42 **39. CROSS WORDS**

Page 43 **40. SECRET WORDS**

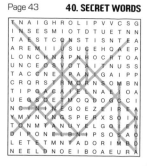

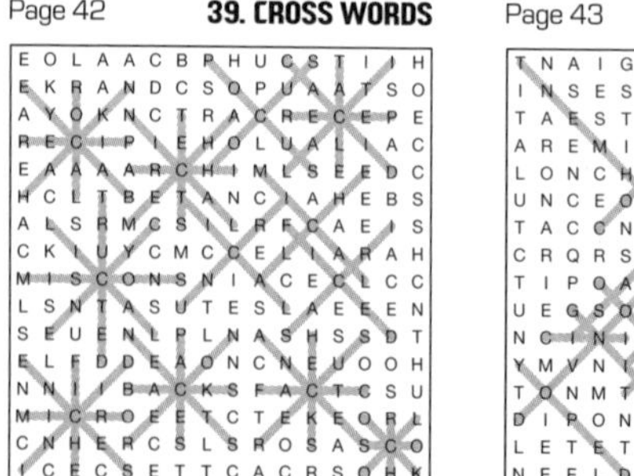

SOLUTIONS

Page 44

41. WRAPAROUND

```
S E R E I I U V G U A E D N E M
N D R I A H A U L A G O P D V U
A S N V R R D A O S U R A L A U
L L G N D R O L V R S O O N N S
E N N N E R N H O D P I U T O L
E U N T D U L S C A R N U I I R
V N N E L T U V S E N R P H R S
N R E P R T I M T I P S D A R E
E E R E S N L S M S I G A S N V
D N M T E A E E D A C N A E E Z
L N E A I I U B E D E A P A P E
A A E E N S A U D V E N E A B U
E O G D E A Z N D I H L O V A R
U L A L R D I A O L M A I V S U
N O B N V E A D U E I S A U R I
O E V I P N S A A A T U D E N O
```

Page 45

42. EMPTY INSIDE

```
R S N L F L S N U T I S P E U S
S S U I T A C U P S U S C M U U
O U U C M O L O T L U A A T A T
U S R T U B P T U A S C A U P R
B O T R I M O M O T L R A S Y O
S N U R I N U S E S T U S P R T
O U S S A C E L T S T U D S O N
R C T U O T L G O R C R U N C I
S A R T T A I R O N A N A S U I
M L L S N A R F I L I T G T M Y
S A L U C I R R O C U M U L U S
U U S E C R M B N R N M B S L S
U F R L M S A U I T M C U U U S
U U T I O O I T L F D I U C S R
L R O P C U A A E E U U S T C U
C A R N L L O R U U V S L U S A
```

Page 46

43. LEFTOVER LETTERS

```
F N D N D N R E I H S I F E B T
N R D L A O D H S E R O T A N N
O N W N O T N A M M W E N T A N
N E N O O A M R O E I S T A N O
D E R D L H H F E D D R H Y O W
A O H N E E Y E F R N N U L E O
M M E L I K N L E O O A L O F A
D I P A V R L W L T H E E H L C
E O B R I O S N G E M P K R R L
L N U A E M E N L M E T O A B H
N R G S R E I L L G R K W O R R
I O R E F H E O E A P F M I L M
R E N T S A N R G N O E R O U L
O N R T N D T T R A W E I T S R
G R A E P S O H R T M O E A B G
A W T D O B R D D O R E A A M M
```

STEALING THE LIMELIGHT

Page 47

44. LITTLE CLUES

```
G N I D D U P K C A L B S I A U
M S B C E B E T I F H N D U B O
M U O O E G L A R K A T O U C O
A E S O I A A U E E B A E R E A
T P G H E L I S B I N L E E O G
O M P R R T E D U O I O G C N G
A E E L S O E D C A P C L I N E
S C E A E K O A E B S O G U W D
T A L F A J B M S G N H O J O E
C A R B G C U T A C G C M E R I
D E P A S T R I E S E U E G B R
D A I N L C H P C U N A L N H F
U O T A M O T G A E T N E A S U
P R T N A S S I O R C I T R A B
P A N C A K E S S D P A T O H N
G G E D E H C A O P G P E G T A
```

APPLE JUICE
BACON
BAKED BEANS
BLACK PUDDING
BOILED EGG
CEREAL
CROISSANT
FRIED EGG
FRUIT SALAD
HASH BROWN
MUSHROOM
OMELETTE
ORANGE JUICE
PAIN AU CHOCOLAT
PANCAKES
PASTRIES
POACHED EGG
SAUSAGE
TOAST
TOMATO

Page 48

45. SECRET WORDS

```
V W B D E S M T V M T E M R R D
E C E E D E A E B Y R A M N I N
X S M A R G R A L I N G N U A E
O O O O O U L H N W R E V T D A
T R W A O I T E I T N E S S B P
N E C O A R E C N A A N D D E E
L C I O O P L G E O E R A W A I
L N G V L D A C E T T U Y W I N
N A A E I R N N E S I I S S M A
O I W R N V C A C N R A N S S L
E D F W N A E W A E O B V P P M
A L E H F A C E H O S I E A H T
A L I I R A A U N I F N E H N E
H O E N N T N E A A P E A B L E
C N S G A H T R D R X L R R P C
E E L M I D F I S A A L L D U P
```

Page 49

46. SHAPED WORDS

```
D E E A H S C O N A R G L A N T
D L D T N S C N D A R R N S C N
E N S A B T H C E I D I I S J G
L C E R S T O Y H S P N S S H D
L I A P E B A B S O G R S A R A
U I H A E M A T N O I L Y H E C
T R N M I R A C I A K I A H S I
A U E S B D A B E C E E P C I N
T N N S P L N N S S E P E R L R
O I P K D R D B N I S N A A E O
L S R E C R O A E O D M B S P E
T F C U R T A N I I O R D Y N H
S O F I I P E H A H Y E U B R A
N O D N B G N H S S R B N G E I
G A L E E L E S E N H L B R N O
E D J I O L M D I E A L Y E E N
```

Page 50

47. WRAPAROUND

```
X N A L I H I L R E A U D R M H
T C E R S F T E C G Q S M L Y R
E M T A I Q P T E U F R L O A S
M I W L G A U I R I R V O O T E
I A O F E R R S T E I E R Y V P
I O L B A T L A S W P B T R A D
E G A L G C N I E G T U R C M L
O M L E P R R O I F L R S T D O
R E R F E O N I O A S L E L P F
L D V E S W S E E S O S A E B N
M I L L O V A T C O A O R I G A
Q U A R T O G T F L E T T E R F
S M C B Q U A W G L A A E C G E
P R D L S S C T T G C E H I T D
E M U E I O F E B M D I E B R R
T L I Y E I E D X M T I E P I R
```

Page 51

48. EMPTY INSIDE

```
N D D T O I L E R O S O E R A L
I T F I D M P S S T A L L E D E
E M A S A E I E T M O D N O K I
I R I O D L L S E E E T O S O U
U D L I O E S L P B O T T F S L
T I U E S V T I A L S E I E I E
A T R O S D E C M R A E T A S A
I D E K O O L R E V O C S A I F
S H T W O E E D S L M R E T L T
P T N K M D N H E I G S R D E O
I C P D N U A F S T G E I E T W
I E L U S M T T V L T H N E E I
L L L I B O O S S U I I T E H B
O B M L U O I U R A O P M S R E
L O E T K M P U S F S O U O L S
N S I U D D L L R W L I F P B F
```

Page 52 **49. SYMBOLIC**

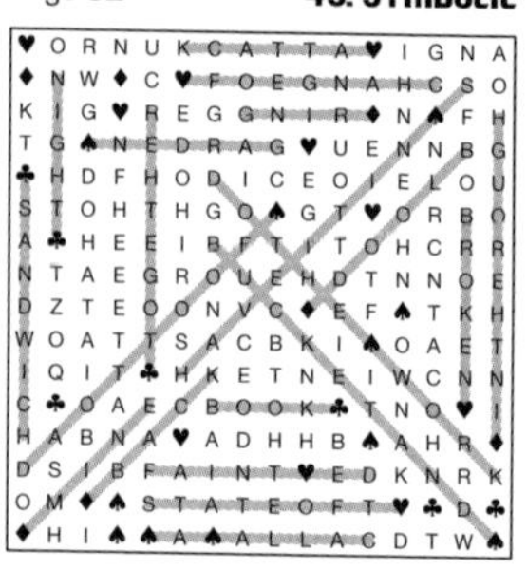

Page 53 **50. WARPED VISION**

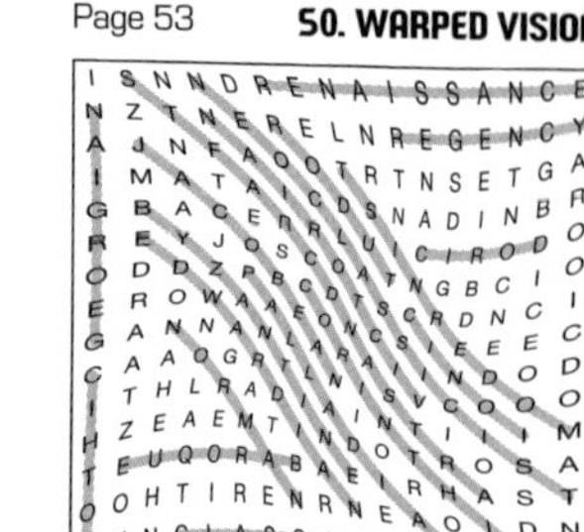

Page 54 **51. LEFTOVER LETTERS**

BRINGING HOME THE BACON

Page 55 **52. SECRET WORDS**

Page 56 **53. SHAPED WORDS**

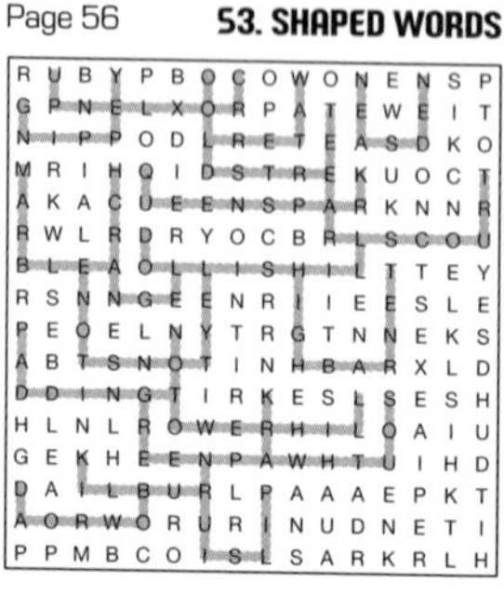

Page 57 **54. LEFTOVER LETTERS**

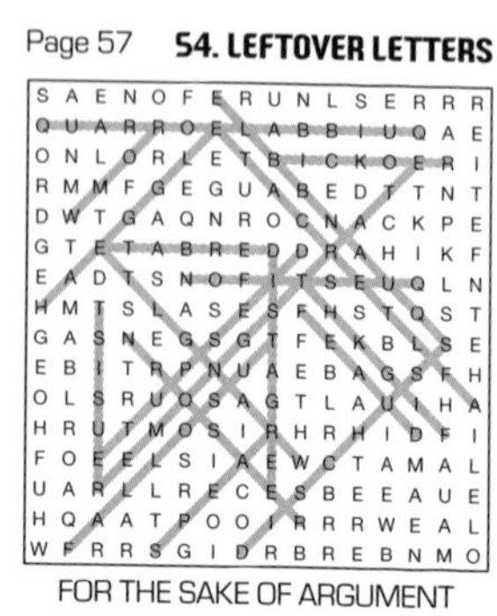

FOR THE SAKE OF ARGUMENT

Page 58 **55. SYMBOLIC**

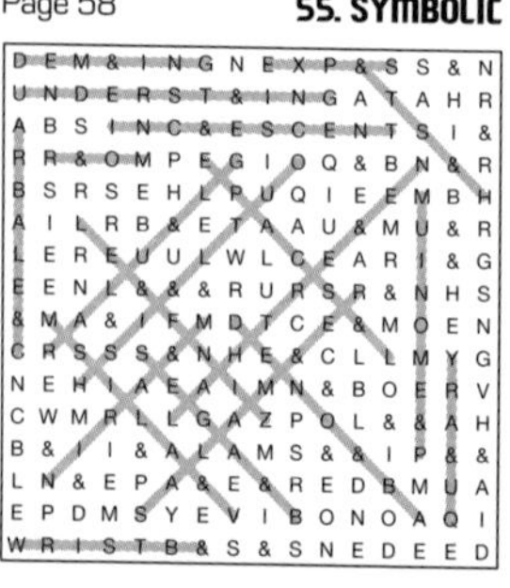

Page 59 **56. LEFTOVER LETTERS**

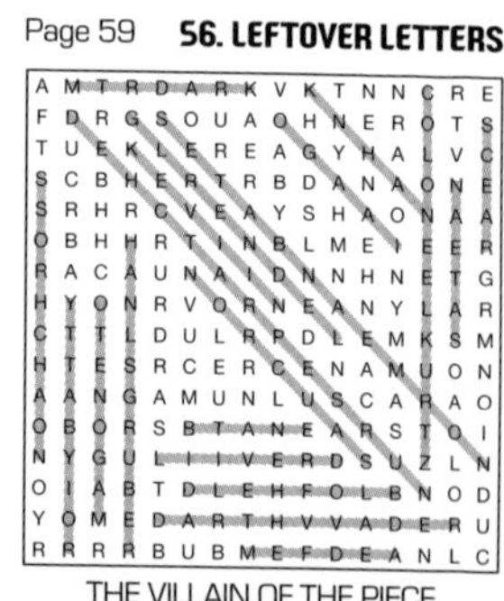

THE VILLAIN OF THE PIECE

Page 60 **57. CROSS WORDS**

Page 61 **58. WRAPAROUND**

Page 62 **59. OFF GRID**

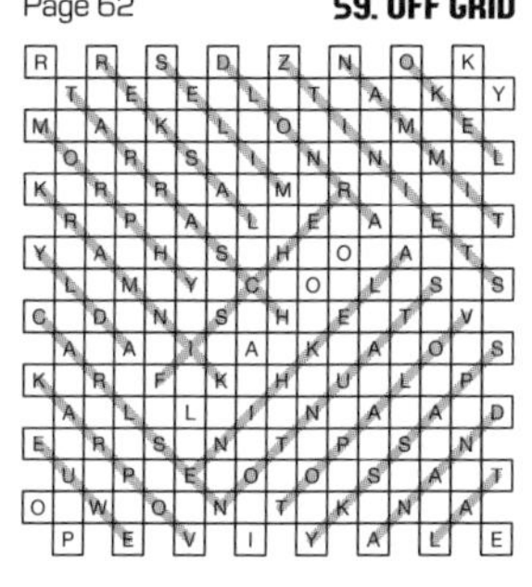

Page 63 **60. SECRET WORDS**

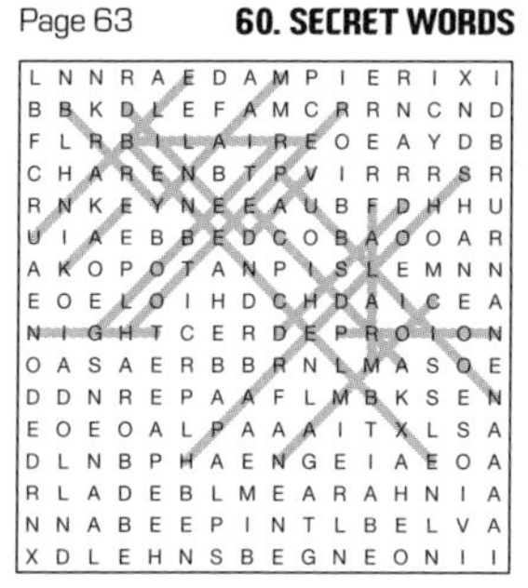

Page 64 **61. WRAPAROUND**

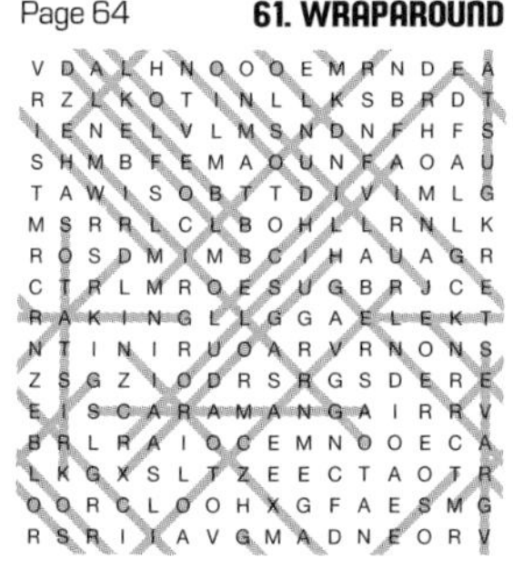

Page 65 **62. LITTLE CLUES**

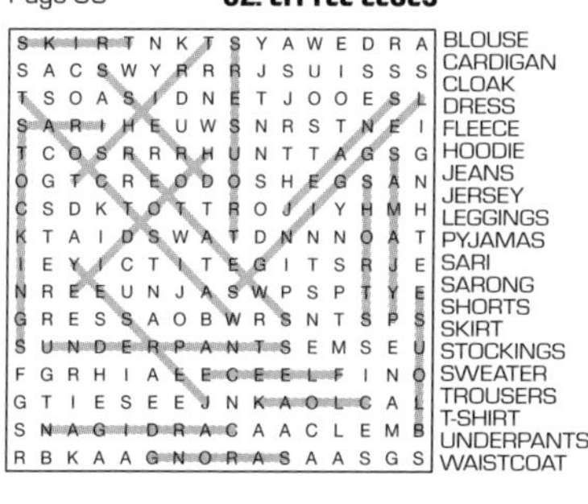

BLOUSE
CARDIGAN
CLOAK
DRESS
FLEECE
HOODIE
JEANS
JERSEY
LEGGINGS
PYJAMAS
SARI
SARONG
SHORTS
SKIRT
STOCKINGS
SWEATER
TROUSERS
T-SHIRT
UNDERPANTS
WAISTCOAT

Page 66 **63. VOWELLESS**

Page 67 **64. THIS AND THAT**

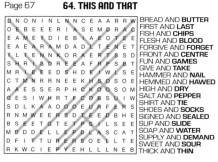

BREAD AND **BUTTER**
FIRST AND **LAST**
FISH AND **CHIPS**
FLESH AND **BLOOD**
FORGIVE AND **FORGET**
FRONT AND **CENTRE**
FUN AND **GAMES**
GIVE AND **TAKE**
HAMMER AND **NAIL**
HEMMED AND **HAWED**
HIGH AND **DRY**
SALT AND **PEPPER**
SHIRT AND **TIE**
SHOES AND **SOCKS**
SIGNED AND **SEALED**
SLIP AND **SLIDE**
SOAP AND **WATER**
SUPPLY AND **DEMAND**
SWEET AND **SOUR**
THICK AND **THIN**

SOLUTIONS

Page 68 **65. LEFTOVER LETTERS**

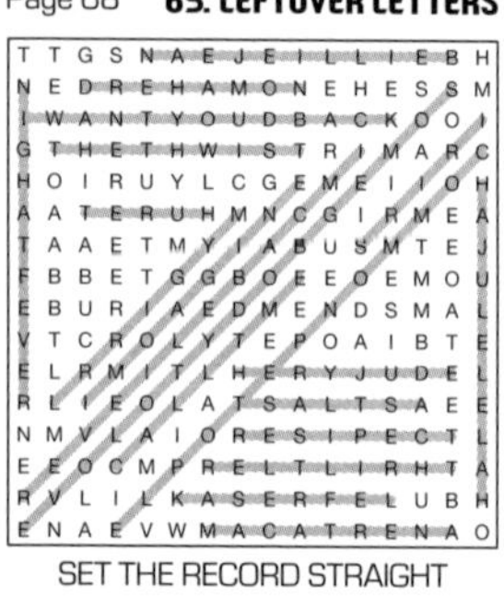

SET THE RECORD STRAIGHT

Page 69 **66. CROSS WORDS**

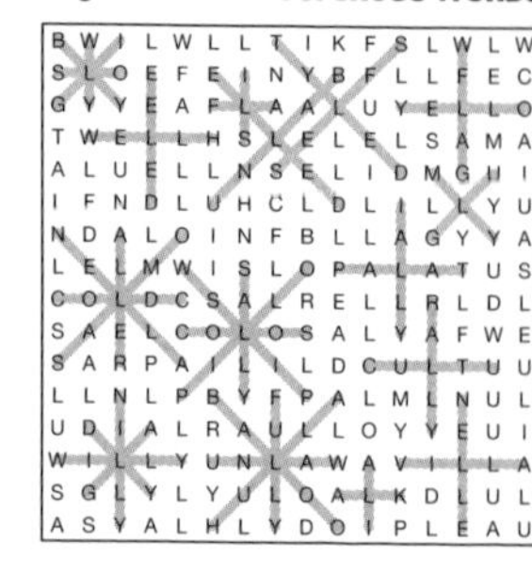

Page 70 **67. WRAPAROUND**

Page 71 **68. SHAPED WORDS**

Page 72 **69. SECRET WORDS**

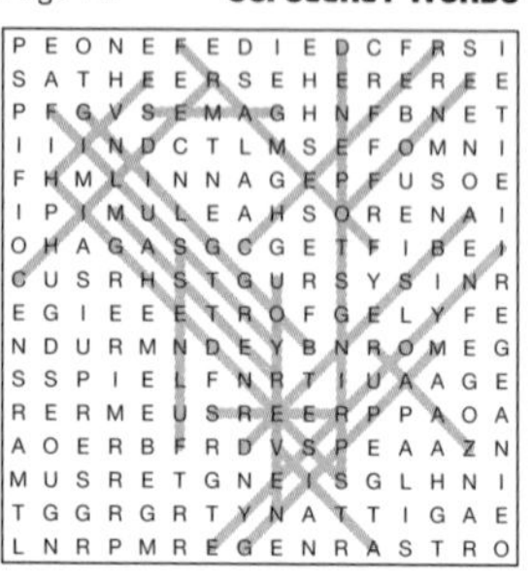

Page 73 **70. WARPED VISION**

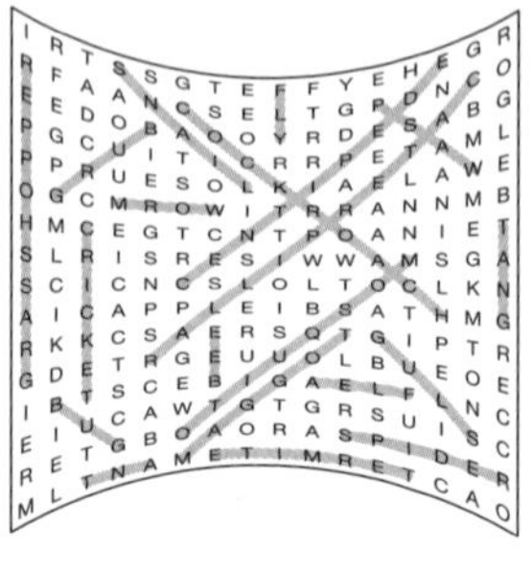

Page 74 **71. LITTLE CLUES**

APPLE
BANANA
BLACKBERRY
CHERRY
ELDERBERRY
GRAPE
KIWI
LEMON
LIME
LYCHEE
MANGO
MELON
NECTARINE
ORANGE
PEACH
PEAR
POMEGRANATE
RASPBERRY
SATSUMA
STRAWBERRY

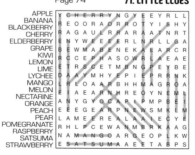

Page 75 **72. SHAPED WORDS**

Page 76

73. CROSS WORDS

```
U A S R R A A C F A U A G T M C
C A Y Z E A G K I C E A T M A M
E R A C R N A A A V J C R C L X
E B A R I U M J C L A E A A A S
S P E F A M A L G E I T M U A R
S C G Z T L T C R M A N E R E A
D E N U A S E L E L C I N A C C
E A N A A R E N R A A A A C A A
S A L O Z R E X A G G T P Y G G
R E C X E B D M T E A C A A E M
L B B C T I A I E E G T A T G I
U I A C F A C V V R C C H A R L
L X A T R L I E X A S P C N O R
E R D L E U A A E T T N C S D A
A E G A S U I D O E A E E V A N
A A L M A R M A V B E M A E L D
```

Page 77

74. SYMBOLIC

```
E B . - B O A R D R A . - E O R
R A - I L Y - P A L S I H C D O
E L S E N E D E N . H E R M I C
I D E E L G A J E A . A E I . I
T E - L - B L - U L K L S . T B
. R N I E N B Y M - S J A . E S
N - Y - N E A E K . O N R R D R
O G A R P G E H P O E L M E L S
C I N R E . E . T C E U E I I A
- . T H R - R - . O - M P L N C
T H I E I C R E E O L - Y A E E
E . . R . S S E R C O C R P B R
D E E O - . . T B P O L K A . .
E E I . I S S C S A S B R C L A
. D K U K D L R E - H I I O A L
R . C S I L E . T R . O C R R S
```

Page 78

75. EMPTY INSIDE

```
O I N O A D S R S P T D T N R T
R T L E C G R T E E H N O H G R
S O H T G N A B S L R O C R N H
A I P N A F G S T B I R I C Y O
E P E E B I A N O A O A Q T P A
A I N M G R S A O T H E R M O S
O S E O N S C P B C R T G T N A
K L S S I T A D G I E B S R A E
E E B Q P A N N N N K U L E C L
T K N U E I I A I C O G S A A K
M H A I E D S S K I O S M O I T
T L I T L K T T I P C P C I T A
C E K O S I E O H S S R C A P E
T C F N O T R P G I A A S T S S
O O A E T S A C T H G Y A H N D
L A N T E R N E C E P P M A B P
```

Page 79

76. LEFTOVER LETTERS

```
M M M N E K L C U Y H Y E F L O
M Y C N D U M U E O A T O L H R
M I E G O C C S E N C R M M R M
E H L R C E K I D N T R C M U N
A O T L A T L E Y N E U W A E Y
G H N C E R C L I E L L R E H O
E A T R E N I G I O C M M R O U
T T D E A R N D C N E L H N Y A
O A L D A H D K C T H G C K E G
Y E E E T U E N I M O W E O E A
O D O L N C M R O U E I C M O M
D M N E E W O R R O M K O T R T
R O E L M N M D E R C T N Y A H
M N O F O K E K A M D E Y T E W
A E I M C T Y A N Y M E S R N M
E M E O M W H U O M E L E W T O
```

RUNNING LIKE CLOCKWORK

Page 80

77. WARPED VISION

```
F D G E D E S E R T T U B E E W
A R E N K C O L B N U E T D I L
S S U L I L R T R D C U P C D T
P N E S U D L E G E A G I R E G
I I H W S G L A R G P C R C T L
L A S R A E E E K G U I I S S S
L R U E C G R R W O T O P S R N
G D L G D R E P E L E R S I D E
N R F S I A E A R C K E E N N E
E W S S S S I D S E E L P K K G
R E O R C I A G L P T P W I G I
R E W O H S C R A O A A O S P S
I P L L A D R G R T S N W C E N
W O F P R L E L C L E A N E R N
P L H E G B G N I K A E L P F D
E D T N E A P O W E R W A S H L
```

Page 81

78. SECRET WORDS

```
S T N O O G C R S K F V N K N E
I D Y N S I P M P L N F K D T I
G E G L I T R I N I M Z R N M N
R S H G L R S N R I K N T S N C
L N G I N C T T L H R T D M R M
R R E I O I I I S O H B I E C T
I T D C I L R T N N M N R R R L
I N E I T I N N M M N T N B L T
C F T O S M R D I M U D E S I R
I N T T I P G C M D R H N C N H
E T I I N R P M T R U G N L R N
C O C G G N V E R E G T N V D P
N L P I R S N C R N E N E U M R
I B C G O R T T M N I B N L N N
I E N R C P C R N E C L N N V I
I U I T N I N Y P T H E D L C G
```

Page 82

79. SHAPED WORDS

```
E D E R I I S E D E C W D G D S
W E L K D E R N E I R R I N E G
L A E N I T U M K N T N D I I N
D E I E R W N E L D W I E L L D
E V E K U G A D N S N I V E E D
I A E N N E V I S S D W I S T W
U V W T I R E W U O T S W I T D
N W E N I G A Y V U N K T I S E
G R P G N E D S N E I S G E W D
S E E L Y I E V A K K A V R I C
M D G G S D I I A I N N I R N G
E R A D R E D D T I G G N R I V
S T I E D A A E D N G T D E E D
D E M P I C U R H S A A N O K S
Y R I T N E R V T N M E R O E D
W C R N E B N E D G D N C E O V
```

Page 83

80. CROSS WORDS

```
A A R B Z L N E L S T L E I A C
W M T I D B I O B I Q D H L T I
N S E T U D C T L R I A M I A B
L C L I E L E W P G M N W T N E
L K A F R I E N I I I I T Y D I
C H I L B E G B L G D T I I Z L
H T N P I R E D A C P N V E A G
C T S E I D M R T T U E N B T L
N T K R W N A L I E N R K S N I
I F L I C K A C O C S I I I H T
E F M N I L L R N S Z O P S E G
A L P G I C T E I V M P I T E D
V I O R U I I M R E P I E A I I
I N T L I Q E R Q I S C H I E F
C V I C D V I H L W E I I N I L
N B M K I V N S B L A R C S L I
```

SOLUTIONS

Page 84

81. THIS AND THAT

ADAM AND **EVE**
ALIVE AND **KICKING**
ANT AND **DEC**
CHEESE AND **WINE**
FRY AND **LAURIE**
HOT AND **BOTHERED**
HUFFING AND **PUFFING**
HUSBAND AND **WIFE**
IN AND **OUT**
JACK AND **JILL**
KNIFE AND **FORK**
LADIES AND **GENTLEMEN**
LAW AND **ORDER**
SHIRT AND **TIE**
SONNY AND **CHER**
TATE AND **LYLE**
TRIAL AND **ERROR**
TRIALS AND **TRIBULATIONS**
UP AND **DOWN**
WAR AND **PEACE**

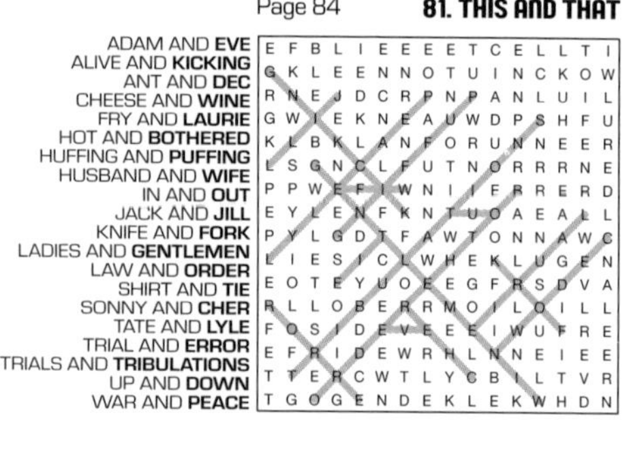

Page 85

82. LEFTOVER LETTERS

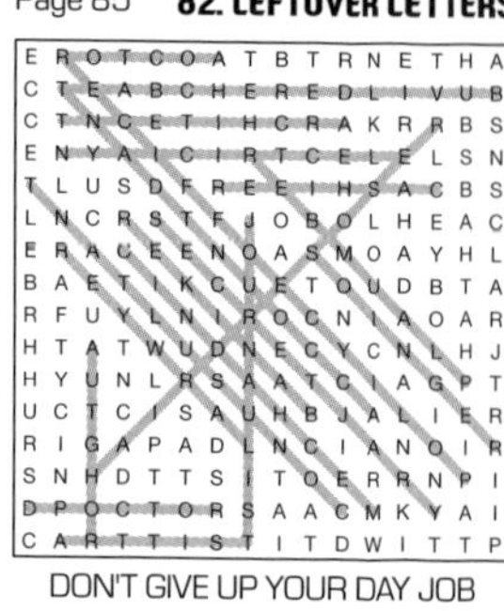

DON'T GIVE UP YOUR DAY JOB

Page 86

83. LITTLE CLUES

AMARYLLIS
BEGONIA
CARNATION
CHRYSANTHEMUM
CLOVER
CORNFLOWER
DAFFODIL
DAISY
DANDELION
FREESIA
GERBERA
IRIS
LILY
ORCHID
PEONY
POPPY
ROSE
SUNFLOWER
SWEET PEA
VIOLET

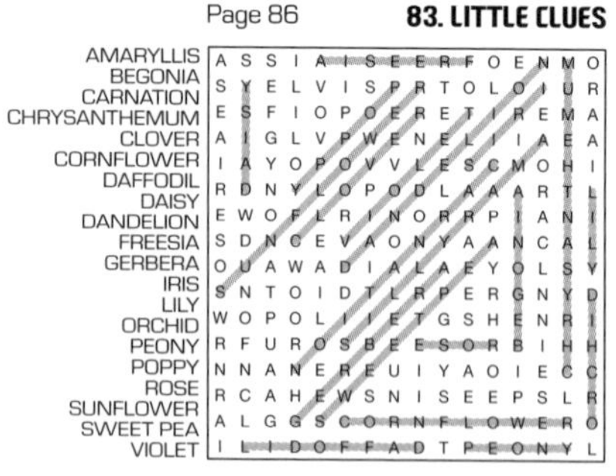

Page 87

84. SECRET WORDS

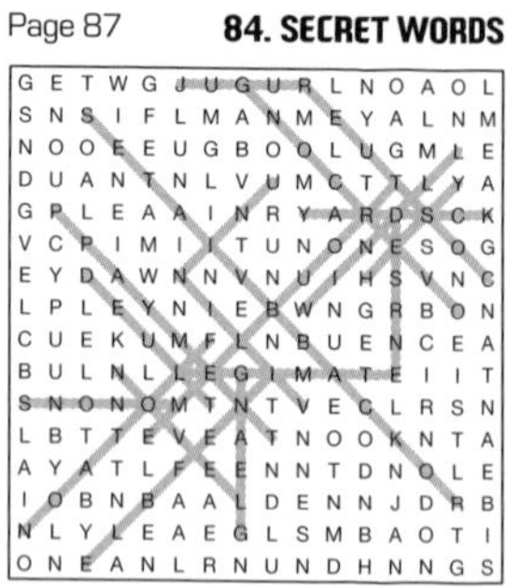

Page 88

85. EMPTY INSIDE

Page 89

86. CROSS WORDS

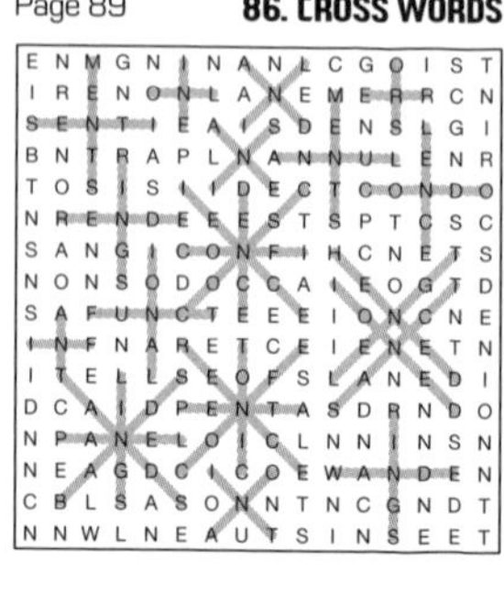

Page 90

87. SHAPED WORDS

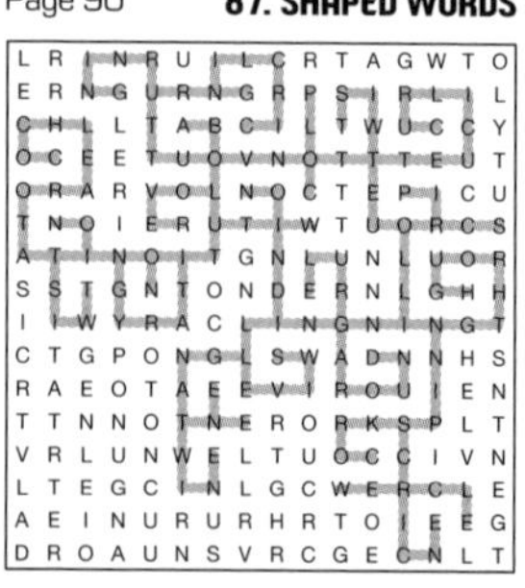

Page 91

88. SYMBOLIC

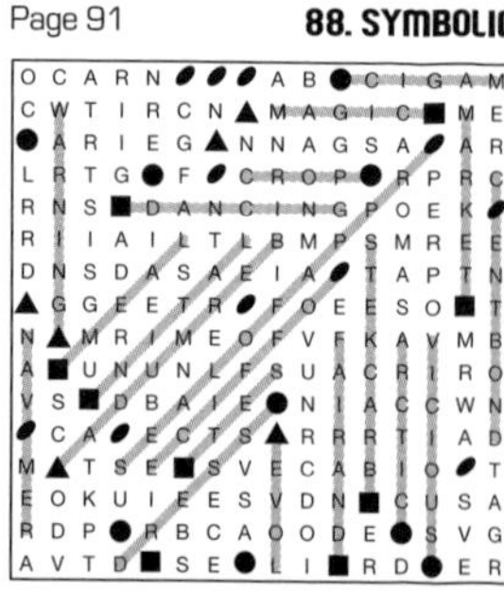

SOLUTIONS

Page 92

89. VOWELLESS

C C R Y S W H P M R M H C M M T
D R L W L C M R H L T S P P L S
M M R D T P F R G T P M H H C C
M N N T G N N N L P S R C W T K
T W N T W N D M L H D H T L L B
R W Z L P N M C F T C R T Z K Z
L B L G T M T M T L S S T G N D
K F C L M S M H C F D T L D M W
P Z G L H R T F B S L C F D R P
N Y S M N L R B S S S F N S H B
K N N M K P S K Y S D B P T F F
W M M D L F L D C B C R F T R K
T C W F S D C H M W W K W L C L
L N G D G N L C T F T C B F R F
N D Y K T B L M T R R R D K K R
C N S K K L C F R N F B R F H B

Page 93

90. WRAPAROUND

E L E G H O L L O R N O B E D I
R E I T L U A G W L I R N L N A
C V L O Z L N I H X C C L I A A
E W D L N E L I I N D O O W T S
S L L I G I L E C R R A A I I N
E M E N O L L T I S L A R O C H
L L C N R R N F L O R C S H O F
K N A B A E N V R I L N Y C R S
S R E V R H L L R I L S N E C A
N A U A I T C R E I N H G B O R
Y L M O E C U L L O H A U E C O
A K K M E C N R C O L A M O C E
A N N L G I L R U L L I E R S L
D E A O Z V E A I T A O I U A O
S S A Z S A C A F O G U C C I F
G I A A G S N N E A E A R C C C

Page 94

91. LEFTOVER LETTERS

C V L D N L D D B O R R L S G Y
A T L A B B A B F N A F B M R T
D N L L I F P N E L R I O L D E
H Y D M W G J A M R E R L R E E
N R N E O B W R I A K M I L T R
T K A S R T A O A S R B S A C D
E T M R O G G O E S C R B I R N
T N E N C N S A J O E A E Y N G
W I A E R H A O L T O M L E T G
I N R C I E I C N I V I A O L A
T O A D I B L R L B H L L I E A
R E M D S C E R M I E L A D L M
D G B E A B B A G E L E E S R S
T L N L L F L N L I D R K O S A
L A L R L L O A M E D E S N H R
L E P S I E N A L S T I S E B N

GREAT MINDS THINK ALIKE

Page 95

92. LITTLE CLUES

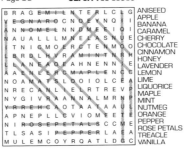

B R A G E M I L N T E R L C L G
V E G N A R O C N O E Y N Q I I
A N N O M E L N N D M E E I Q I
N A U A L L L M N E L A S N U E
I T N I C M O E R C T E N M O O
L B R D L H V R A M I N T N R H
L L A N E A O E A H N E N N I E
A A E N L E R C M A P L E N C C
N O A M A T S L O O I O L C E A
N R E C A N L I E L R T R E V P
N Y G I V R A A N N A L M R N P
Y R R E H C A O T A A T A A U L
A P N E P L L C V I O M E E T E
N I R O S E P E T A L S C C M E
T L S A S I P E P P E R L A E A
M U L E M C O Y R Q A T L D G C

ANISEED
APPLE
BANANA
CARAMEL
CHERRY
CHOCOLATE
CINNAMON
HONEY
LAVENDER
LEMON
LIME
LIQUORICE
MAPLE
MINT
NUTMEG
ORANGE
PEPPER
ROSE PETALS
TREACLE
VANILLA

Page 96

93. CROSS WORDS

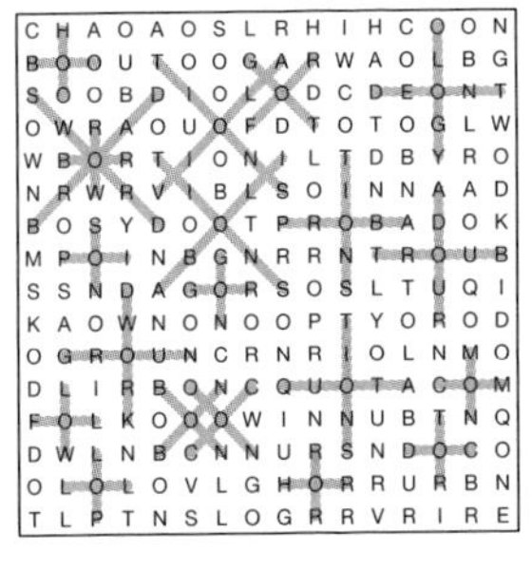

C H A O A O S L R H I H C O O N
B O O U T O O G A R W A O L B G
S O O B D I O L O D C D E O N T
O W R A O U O F D T O T O G L W
W B O R T I O N I L T D B Y R O
N R W R V I B L S O I N N A A D
B O S Y D O O T P R O B A D O K
M P O I N B G N R R N T R O U B
S S N D A G O R S O S L T U Q I
K A O W N O N O O P T Y O R O D
O G R O U N C R N R I O L N M O
D L I R B O N C Q U O T A C O M
F O L K O O O W I N N U B T N Q
D W L N B C N N U R S N D O C O
O L O L O V L G H O R R U R B N
T L P T N S L O G R R V R I R E

Page 97

94. LITTLE CLUES

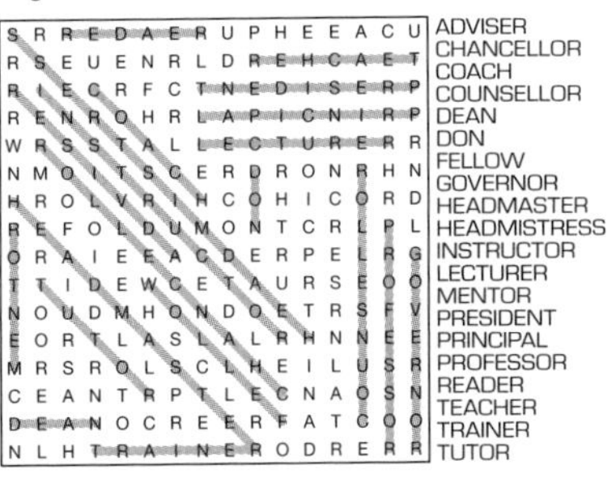

S R R E D A E R U P H E E A C U
R S E U E N R L D R E H C A E T
R I E C R F C T N E D I S E R P
R E N R O H R L A P I C N I R P
W R S S T A L L E C T U R E R R
N M O I T S C E R D R O N R H N
H R O L V R I H C O H I C O R D
R E F O L D U M O N T C R L P L
O R A I E E A C D E R P E L R G
T T I D E W C E T A U R S E O O
N O U D M H O N D O E T R S F V
E O R T L A S L A R H N N E E E
M R S R O L S C L H E I L U S R
C E A N T R P T L E C N A O S N
D E A N O C R E E R F A T C O O
N L H T R A I N E R O D R E R R

ADVISER
CHANCELLOR
COACH
COUNSELLOR
DEAN
DON
FELLOW
GOVERNOR
HEADMASTER
HEADMISTRESS
INSTRUCTOR
LECTURER
MENTOR
PRESIDENT
PRINCIPAL
PROFESSOR
READER
TEACHER
TRAINER
TUTOR

Page 98

95. WRAPAROUND

O B R L B E E C N F S E L B W S
O N E A S R T O S T K L K I E R
A R G D G C I E N A U C L N N L
L S C E U S H D U B A R I E H I
F E R R N L W I G L O W Y L W C
V E G E E L E B E B W E E U R
W R T C D S M E R W W U Y T O T
T X S O E I L A U V S T W R E Y
E S K I E E P E R R E E L T W R
B L F Y R Y T S N F E W B I T E
A I L B F P R N A N N S F U B Y
E E F O W S T S S C E E V T B H
B H U L W L T R E S L F I E C B
T L B E B T H U T C V S E E B L
E N L T O N C E N E P E T M D G
C R X A D W Y E F I M S E T D L

Page 99

96. OFF GRID

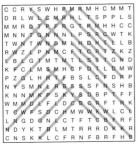

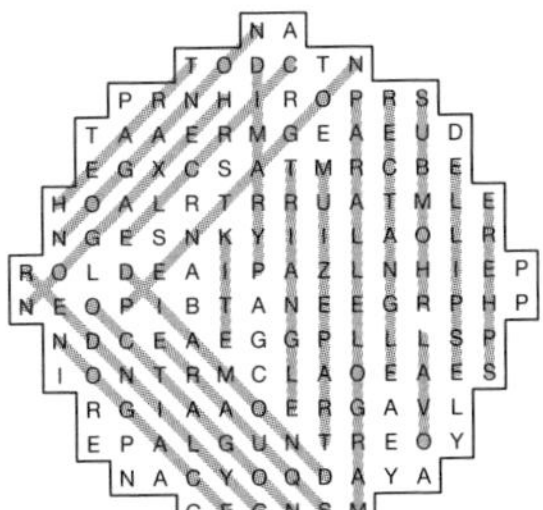

SOLUTIONS

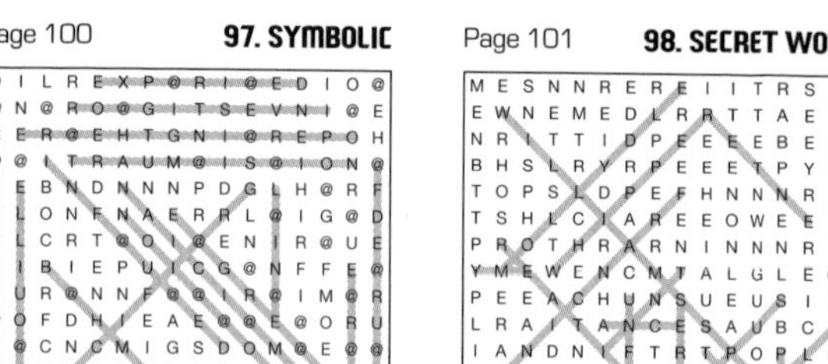

Page 100 **97. SYMBOLIC**

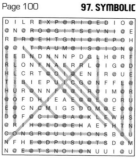

Page 101 **98. SECRET WORDS**

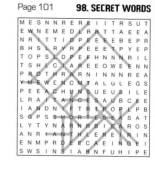

Page 102 **99. LEFTOVER LETTERS**

PUT TWO AND TWO TOGETHER

Page 103 **100. SHAPED WORDS**

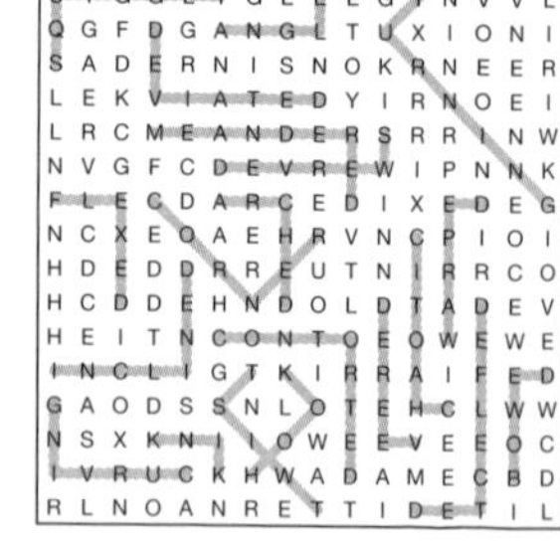

Page 104 **101. CROSS WORDS**

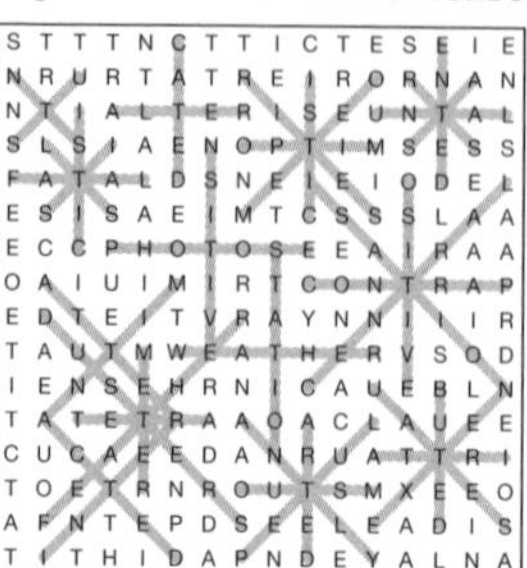

Page 105 **102. SYMBOLIC**

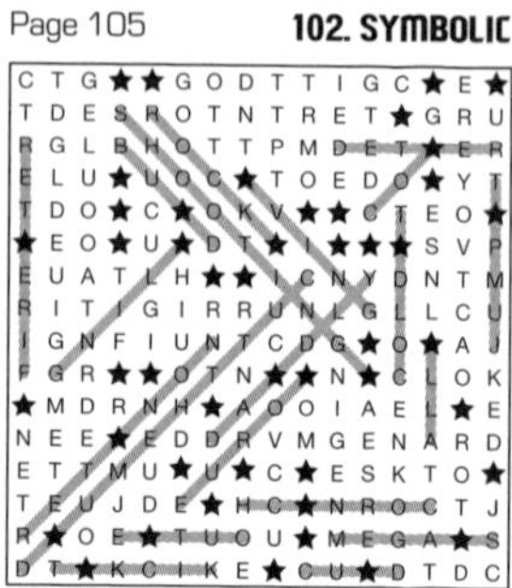

Page 106 **103. LITTLE CLUES**

Page 107 **104. LEFTOVER LETTERS**

ACCIDENT AND EMERGENCY

Page 108 **105. SHAPED WORDS**

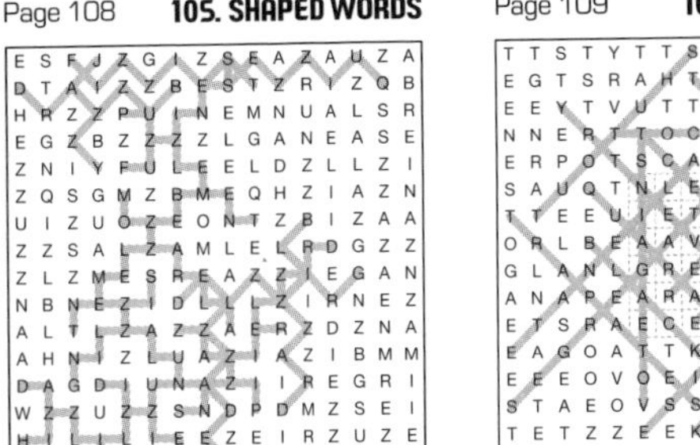

Page 109 **106. EMPTY INSIDE**

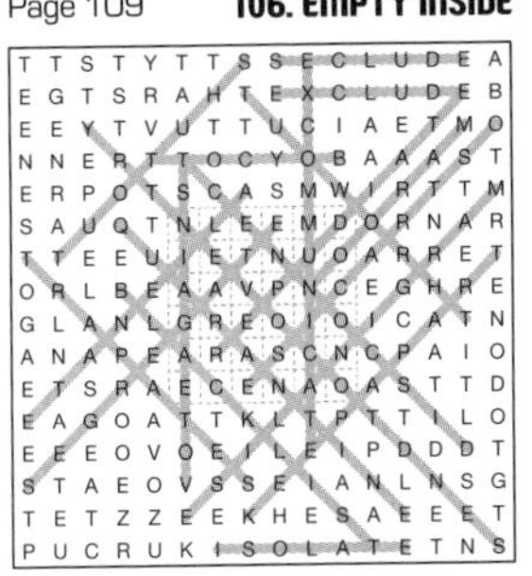

Page 110 **107. CROSS WORDS**

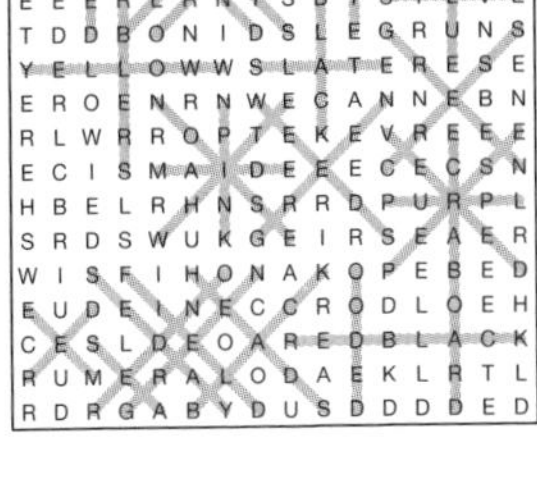

Page 111 **108. WARPED VISION**

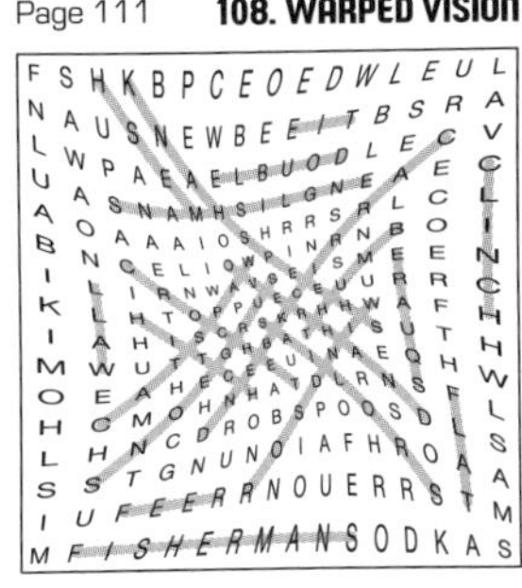

Page 112 **109. VOWELLESS**

Page 113 **110. LITTLE CLUES**

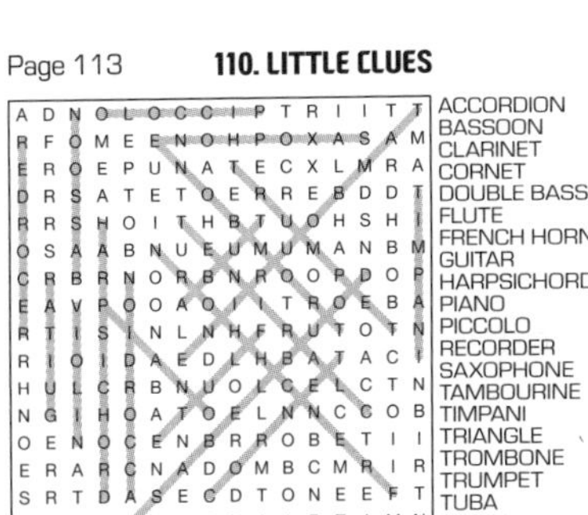

If you enjoyed **TWISTED WORD SEARCH** why not give **TWISTED SUDOKU** a whirl next?

TWISTED WORD SEARCH

U S H L
I A D
L E N S
E H P D Y
O F M
F N I Y